HANDBOOK

NUMBER FOU

The United Kingdom Mathematics Trust

Introduction to Number Theory

Published by The United Kingdom Mathematics Trust.
Maths Challenges Office, School of Mathematics, University of Leeds,
Leeds, LS2 9JT, United Kingdom

http://www.ukmt.org.uk

First published 2006.
Second edition published 2010.

ISBN 978-1-906001-12-4

Printed in the UK for the UKMT by The Charlesworth Group, Wakefield.

http://www.charlesworth.com

Typographic design by Andrew Jobbings of Arbelos.

http://www.arbelos.co.uk

Typeset with LaTeX.

The books published by the United Kingdom Mathematics Trust are grouped into series.

The EXCURSIONS IN MATHEMATICS series consists of monographs which focus on a particular topic of interest and investigate it in some detail, using a wide range of ideas and techniques. They are aimed at high school students, undergraduates and others who are prepared to pursue a subject in some depth, but do not require specialised knowledge.

1. *The Backbone of Pascal's Triangle,* Martin Griffiths

The HANDBOOKS series is aimed particularly at students at secondary school who are interested in acquiring the knowledge and skills which are useful for tackling challenging problems, such as those posed in the competitions administered by the UKMT and similar organisations.

1. *Plane Euclidean Geometry: Theory and Problems,* A D Gardiner and C J Bradley
2. *Introduction to Inequalities,* C J Bradley
3. *A Mathematical Olympiad Primer,* Geoff C Smith
4. *Introduction to Number Theory,* C J Bradley

The PATHWAYS series aims to provide classroom teaching material for use in secondary schools. Each title develops a subject in more depth and in more detail than is normally required by public examinations or national curricula.

1. *Crossing the Bridge,* Gerry Leversha

The PROBLEMS series consists of collections of high-quality and original problems of Olympiad standard.

1. *New Problems in Euclidean Geometry,* David Monk

The YEARBOOKS series documents all the UKMT activities, including details of all the challenge papers and solutions, lists of high scorers, accounts of the IMO and Olympiad training camps, and other information about the Trust's work during each year.

Contents

II Solving problems 97

Series Editor's Foreword

This book is part of a series whose aim is to help young mathematicians prepare for competitions, such as the British Mathematical Olympiad, at secondary school level. Like other volumes in the Handbooks series, it provides cheap and ready access to directly relevant material. All these books are characterised by the large number of carefully constructed exercises for the reader to attempt.

In its original form, this was presented as part of the composite volume Introductions to Number Theory and Inequalities. It has now been extensively revised and reorganised, with more examples and exercises, and is now published as a single volume dedicated to Number Theory . This work has been undertaken by James Gazet, Nick Lord and myself, with the blessing of the original author C J Bradley.

I hope that every secondary school will have these books in its library. The prices have been set so low that many good students will wish to purchase their own copies. Schools wishing to give out large numbers of copies as these books as prizes should note that discounts may be negotiated with the UKMT office.

London, UK GERRY LEVERSHA

About the author

C J Bradley is a prolific author of questions for mathematics competitions, and played an important role on the Problems Selection Committee of IMO 2002 in Glasgow. He was formerly a University Lecturer in the University of Oxford and Official Fellow and Tutor at Jesus College. He was Deputy Leader of the UK Mathematical Olympiad Team from 1992 to

1995, and is still involved in training the team for the annual International Mathematical Olympiad. He was for many years a teacher at Clifton College, Bristol.

About the editors

James Gazet runs one of the Summer Schools for the UKMT as well as acting as a marker for both the BMO and IMOK Olympiad competitions. He is currently head of mathematics at Eton College.

Gerry Leversha is Editor of *The Mathematical Gazette*, and teaches at St Paul's School in London. He has been involved in the UKMT as Chair of Publications and on the setting panel for the BMO and IMOK Olympiads and has been involved in the training of the UK IMO squad.

Nick Lord is Editor of the Problem Corner of *The Mathematical Gazette* and teaches at Tonbridge School in Kent. He has been involved in the UKMT as a member of Council and a marker for the IMOK Olympiads.

Preface

The purpose of this book is to provide talented students with more challenging material than exists in secondary school syllabuses. The age range targeted is 15 to 18 years, though some who are younger would also benefit. The commentary is very full, with complete solutions to all exercises, together with additional insights. Although most readers will probably benefit from contact with an experienced expert, an exceptional student may well manage without any outside help. An alternative use for this material may be in Maths Clubs, where more guidance is available and a wider ability range is involved.

A number of theorems in this book are stated without proof. They may be found in many excellent textbooks, for example, *A Friendly Introduction to Number Theory* by Silverman [6]. Another book that I heartily recommend is *An Introduction to the Theory of Numbers* by Niven, Zuckerman and Montgomery [5]. I am grateful to Professor Adam McBride of the University of Strathclyde, Professor Jim Wiegold of the University of Wales, Cardiff (who died in August 2009), Dr Brian Wilson of Royal Holloway College of the University of London and Dr Geoff Smith of the University of Bath for working through the original manuscript and making helpful comments and suggestions for improvement.

Bristol C J BRADLEY

Part I

Theory

Chapter 1

Divisibility and prime numbers

1.1 The natural numbers

The *natural numbers*, which are sometimes called the counting numbers or the whole numbers, consist of

$$1, 2, 3, 4, 5, 6, 7, \ldots, n, \ldots$$

The set of such numbers is denoted by $\mathbb{N}$. Because the natural numbers are arranged in order and adjacent ones have difference of 1, it follows that if $n > m$, then $n \geq m + 1$.

The *integers* are comprised of the natural numbers, their negatives and zero and therefore consist of

$$0, \pm 1, \pm 2, \pm 3, \pm 4, \ldots, \pm n, \ldots$$

The set of such numbers is denoted by $\mathbb{Z}$. The positive integers and the natural numbers are the same set.

An integer a is said to be *divisible* by an integer b if there exists an integer q such that $a = bq$. A useful notation is $b \mid a$, meaning b divides a. The quantity q is sometimes called the *quotient*. Sometimes the words *dividend* and *divisor* are used for a and b respectively. Thus 21 is divisible by 7, or $7 \mid 21$, with quotient 3. We also say 7 is a *factor* of 21 and 21 is a *multiple* of 7. Note that 0 is divisible by all integers. However, you cannot divide any non-zero integer by 0.

Theorem 1.1 *If $d \mid a$ and $d \mid b$ then $d \mid (xa + yb)$ for all integers x and y.*

PROOF If $d \mid a$ and $d \mid b$, then $a = md$ and $b = nd$. Thus

$$xa + yb = xmd + ynd = (xm + yn)d$$

and hence $d \mid (xa + yb)$. ❑

For example, if a and b are both multiples of 5 then so is any linear combination of a and b. It is often sensible to prove properly things that for a long time we have taken for granted.

1.2 The Euclidean algorithm

Suppose a and b are integers with $a > b \geq 1$. Then $(a+1)b > ab \geq a$, so there are positive multiples of b that are greater than a. We take it as axiomatic that a non-empty subset of the positive integers has a least member. In mathematics this is called the *principle of well-ordering*. So there is a least integer $(q+1)$ such that $(q+1)b > a$. It follows that $qb \leq a$ and hence $a = qb + r$, where $0 \leq r$. Also $r < b$ since $(q+1)b > a$. We may therefore write

$$a = qb + r, \quad \text{where } 0 \leq r < b. \tag{1.1}$$

For example,

$$17 = 3 \times 5 + 2$$
$$2008 = 286 \times 7 + 6.$$

The ability to divide a positive integer by another one and to produce a quotient and a non-negative remainder less than the divisor is so commonplace that it is scarcely thought of as being remarkable. But in fact what we are really doing is to say that given any two positive integers a and b with $a > b \geq 1$, then there exist integers Q such that $Qb > a$ and that the set of all such integers Q has a least member namely $(q+1)$.

Equation (1.1) is the heart of the *Euclidean algorithm* which works as follows. If $r \neq 0$, then since b and r are positive integers with $b > r \geq 1$, the Euclidean algorithm can be applied again using b and r. And the process can be repeated again and again until we get a remainder that is zero. Since the remainder is always less than the divisor, each step of the process involves a non-negative integer remainder which is less than that of the previous step. The process must therefore terminate after a finite number of steps, and consequently can be called an algorithm.

Example 1.1 Let us apply this algorithm when $a = 893$ and $b = 705$. We have

$$
\begin{aligned}
893 &= 1 \times 705 + 188, \\
705 &= 3 \times 188 + 141, \\
188 &= 1 \times 141 + 47, \\
141 &= 3 \times 47 + 0.
\end{aligned}
$$

1.3 Highest common factor and lowest common multiple

The *highest common factor* (also called the greatest common divisor) of two positive integers a and b is defined to be the positive integer d such that

(i) d divides both a and b, and
(ii) if c is any other factor of a and b, then c divides d.

The notation $d = (a, b)$ is often used.

If $(a, b) = 1$ then a and b are said to be *coprime* or *relatively prime*. Hence 21 and 16 are coprime. Repeated use of the Euclidean algorithm provides the highest common factor as the last non-zero remainder. An exceptional case is when one of a and b is an exact multiple of the other, in which case the highest common factor is the smaller of the two. Of course, if $a = b$, then $(a, b) = a$.

Thus $(893, 705) = 47$. The claim that 47 is the highest common factor arises from the following argument which makes repeated use of theorem 1.1. First 47 divides 141 and hence divides 188. It divides 141 and 188, so it divides 705. It divides 188 and 705 and so it divides 893. 47 is therefore a factor of 705 and 893. Secondly, working the other way round, if c divides both 893 and 705 it must divide 188. Since c divides both 705 and 188 it must divide 141 and hence in turn it must divide 47. Therefore 47 satisfies both property (i) and property (ii) of the above definition and is the highest common factor. The (slightly damaged) argument that repeated use of the Euclidean algorithm always provides the highest common factor as the last non-zero remainder follows precisely the same form as that used for 893 and 705. To write the argument out in detail using letters rather than numbers provides no further insight and so is omitted.

If $a \mid m$ and $b \mid m$ them m is a common multiple of a and b. If m has the properties

(i) that it is a common multiple of a and b, and
(ii) $m \mid n$ whenever n is a common multiple of a and b,

then m is called the *lowest common multiple* of a and b (also called the least common multiple). The notation $m = [a, b]$ is often used.

The lowest common multiple of 893 and 705 is 13 395.

Example 1.2 We prove that 75 and 34 are coprime.

We have

$$\begin{aligned} 75 &= 2 \times 34 + 7, \\ 34 &= 4 \times 7 + 6, \\ 7 &= 1 \times 6 + 1, \\ 6 &= 6 \times 1. \end{aligned}$$

Since 1 is the last non-zero remainder 75 and 34 are coprime.

It is possible to extend these ideas to the case of three or more positive integers. The *highest common factor* of a, b and c is defined to be the positive integer d such that

(i) d divides each of a, b and c
(ii) if c is any other common factor of a, b and c, then c divides d.

If their highest common factor is 1, then a, b and c are said to be *mutually coprime*. However, this is not the same as saying that a, b and c are coprime in pairs. Consider, for instance, the case of the three integers 6, 10 and 15. These are mutually coprime, but none of the three pairs are coprime.

1.4 Linear Diophantine equations

The working in example 1.2 may be recast as follows:

$$\begin{aligned}1 &= 7 - 1 \times 6 \\ &= 7 - 1 \times (34 - 4 \times 7) \\ &= 5 \times 7 - 1 \times 34 \\ &= 5 \times (75 - 2 \times 34) - 1 \times 34 \\ &= 5 \times 75 - 11 \times 34.\end{aligned}$$

In terms of $a = 75$ and $b = 34$, we have $xa + yb = 1$, where $x = 5$ and $y = -11$.

Theorem 1.2 *If a and b are coprime positive integers, then there exist integers x and y such that $xa + yb = 1$.*

The proof is constructive, using the Euclidean algorithm in reverse, as in the example above, and is therefore omitted.

Theorem 1.2 has a significant consequence.

Theorem 1.3 *If a and m are coprime and a is a factor of mn, then a is a factor of n.*

PROOF By theorem 1.2, there exist integers x and y such that $xa + my = 1$. Since a is a factor of mn, there is an integer k such that $mn = ak$. Hence $aky = mny = n(1 - xa)$, so that

$$n = aky + anx = a(ky + nx)$$

and therefore a is a factor of n. ❑

Equations whose solutions are required to be integers are known as *Diophantine equations* (after the Greek mathematician Diophantus).

Theorem 1.4 *The equation*

$$ax + by = n \tag{1.2}$$

has integer solutions if, and only if, (a, b) is a factor of n.

PROOF If $n = 0$, we have the trivial solution $x = 0, y = 0$.

Suppose that $n \neq 0$. Then it is clear that if equation (1.2) has a solution, then (a, b) divides into the left-hand side, and therefore is a factor of n.

If, conversely, (a, b) is a factor of n, then we can divide equation (1.2) through by (a, b) to produce a new (equivalent) equation $a'x + b'y = n'$, in which $(a', b') = 1$ and n' is an integer. Now by theorem 1.2 this equation has solutions in integers. ❑

Returning to example 1.2, we see that the equation $75x + 34y = 1$ has the solution $x = 5$, $y = -11$. It is now easy to construct an infinite set of solutions, since we can add any multiple of 34 to x and subtract the same multiple of 75 from y. In fact, this procedure finds all solutions of the equation. This is formalised in the following theorem.

Theorem 1.5 *Suppose* $n \neq 0$ *and* $h = (a, b)$ *is a factor of* n*. The general solution of the equation* (1.2) *is*

$$x = x_0 + \frac{kb}{h}, \quad y = y_0 - \frac{ka}{h},$$

where k *is an integer and* x_0, y_0 *is one solution of equation* (1.2).

PROOF The solution x_0, y_0 exists by theorem 1.2 and then it is clear that $x = x_0 + \frac{kb}{h}, y = y_0 - \frac{ka}{h}$ are also solutions.

For clarity we will write $a' = \frac{a}{h}, b' = \frac{b}{h}$ noting that $(a', b') = 1$.

Suppose that there is another solution x_1, y_1 not in the list. Then x_1 lies between two adjacent values of x in the list, so that $x_1 = x_2 + u$, say, where $0 < u < b'$ and x_2, y_2 is a solution in the list. Now

$$a'x_1 + b'y_1 = a'x_2 + b'y_2$$

so that

$$a'(x_1 - x_2) = b'(y_2 - y_1),$$

that is,

$$a'u = b'(y_2 - y_1).$$

Since $(a', b') = 1$ it follows from theorem 1.3 that $b' \mid u$. But this contradicts our earlier assumption that $0 < u < b'$. ❑

Exercise 1a

In the exercises below you should not express integers as products of their prime factors since we have not yet shown that such factorisations are unique. You should only use the concepts we have covered so far.

1. Find the highest common factor h of 630 and 765 using the Euclidean algorithm.

2. Find the integers s and t such that $630 = hs$ and $765 = ht$ and prove that s and t are coprime. Prove that $[s, t] = st$ and hence find the lowest common multiple of 630 and 765.

3. Verify that $630 \times 765 = (765, 630) \times [765, 630]$.

4. Is it true that $ab = (a, b) \times [a, b]$ for all positive integers a, b? If so, prove it.

5. Prove that $[893, 705] = 13\,395$.

6. Find the solution sets for the following Diophantine equations.

(a) $7x + 4y = 1$

(b) $35x + 12y = 1$

(c) $133x + 84y = 1$

7. What is the smallest positive integer h for which x and y can be found such that $133x + 84y = h$?

8. A pair of scales is provided with an arbitrarily large quantity of 7 g and 4 g weights. What are the weights of objects which can be accurately ascertained

(a) if one or more weights can be placed in the pan where the object is put (with weights in the other pan) and

(b) if the weights must be put in the pan only on the other side to that of the object being weighed?

9. Given non-zero integers $a_1, a_2, \ldots, a_n$, show that $(a_1, a_2, \ldots, a_n)$ is the smallest positive integer which can be expressed in the form $a_1x_1 + a_2x_2 + \cdots + a_nx_n$, for integers $x_1, x_2, \ldots, x_n$.

Deduce that the Diophantine equation $a_1x_1 + a_2x_2 + \cdots + a_nx_n = b$ is soluble if, and only if, $(a_1, a_2, \ldots, a_n) \mid b$.

1.5 Primes, irreducibles and units

We define a *prime number* p to be a positive integer bigger than 1 such that given integers m and n, if $p \mid mn$, then either $p \mid m$ or $p \mid n$.

We define an *irreducible* to be an integer t which is neither 1 nor -1, and has property that t is divisible only by ± 1 and $\pm t$. The integers that divide 1 are called *units* and consist of ± 1. The primes and irreducibles have been defined so as not to include the units.

Theorem 1.6 *A prime number is an irreducible.*

PROOF If p is prime and $p = mn$, then $p \mid mn$ and so $p \mid m$ or $p \mid n$. If $p \mid m$, then $m = cp$ and so $p = pcn$, and since $p \neq 0$, we have $cn = 1$ and so $c = n = 1$ or $c = n = -1$. A similar argument applies if $p \mid n$. Hence if m divides p, then $m = \pm 1$ or $\pm p$. ❑

Later we will show that all positive irreducibles are prime. So why, you may ask, introduce two different words to define such similar objects: the irreducibles are just the positive and negative primes. The answer lies in a generalisation of number systems in which 'integers' may exist, but in which primes and irreducibles are very different things.

Theorem 1.7 *An irreducible integer is a prime.*

PROOF Suppose that t is irreducible and that $t \mid mn$. Suppose also that t does not divide m. Since the only factors of t are ± 1 and $\pm t$ this means that t and m are coprime. It follows from theorem 1.2 that integers x and y exist such that $xt + ym = 1$. Hence $xtn + ymn = n$. Now $t \mid xtn$ and $t \mid ymn$ and hence, by theorem 1.1, $t \mid n$. It follows that t is prime. ❑

The equivalence of positive irreducibles and primes is crucially important in the arithmetic of integers, as it allows us to prove that the factorisation of a positive integer into irreducible positive integers can be done in one and only one way.

Theorem 1.8 (Fundamental theorem of arithmetic) *If N a positive integer, then N is either 1, a prime, or a product of primes (positive irreducibles). Suppose that* $N = p_1 p_2 \dots p_n = q_1 q_2 q_3 \dots q_m$, *where the* $p_j, j = 1$ *to* n *and* $q_k, k = 1$ *to* m *are primes, then* $n = m$ *and the* q_k *are a permutation of the* p_j. *(Note that the* p_j *and* q_k *are not necessarily distinct since powers of primes may occur).*

PROOF Though the proof is technically complicated, the ideas are simple enough. First you have to justify the first sentence. How could it fail? Only if there is at least one positive integer for which the sentence is false. Thus there is a non-empty set of positive integers for which the sentence is false. Now invoke the well-ordering principle. There must be a least positive integer M which violates the conditions. Now M is neither 1 nor a prime (i.e. a positive irreducible). Thus $M = M_1M_2$ where both M_1 and M_2 are smaller than M. Thus for M_1 and M_2 the first sentence applies. It therefore applies to M_1M_2 which is impossible because this is M. We have deduced a contradiction from the assumption that there is at least one positive integer for which the first sentence is false. Therefore the first sentence is a true assertion about the positive integers.

Now suppose you have two rival such factorisations. Then you cancel out any common factors. If you can completely cancel out, you have proved the uniqueness of factorisation. Otherwise you are not left with $1 = 1$ so there are some primes remaining on the left, and some remaining on the right, and those on the left are different from those on the right. Therefore some p_k divides a product of some of the primes q_j. Relabel the primes on the right so that the remaining ones are $q_1, q_2, \ldots, q_t$. Since the p_k is irreducible and $p_k \mid q_1q_2 \cdots q_t$, it follows that $p_1 \mid q_1$ or $p_1 \mid q_2 \cdots q_t$. Repeating this argument again and again we establish that p_k divides some q_j. But q_j is irreducible and $p_k \neq 1$, so $p_k = q_j$ which is absurd. This contradiction establishes the result. ❑

It is normal to write the *prime factorisation* of a positive integer N in the form

$$N = p_1^{\alpha_1} p_2^{\alpha_2} \cdots p_n^{\alpha_n},$$

where $p_1 < p_2 < \cdots < p_n$ and $\alpha_i > 1$. The power α_i is known as the *multiplicity* of the prime p_i.

There are several obvious consequences:

(i) the prime factorisation of MN is the product of the prime factorisations of M and N;

(ii) an integer N is a perfect square if, and only if, all the α_i are even.

Theorem 1.8 has a number of important consequences.

Theorem 1.9 *If M and N are coprime and MN is a perfect square, then M and N are perfect squares.*

PROOF When a perfect square MN is factorised into coprime factors, the primes $p_1, p_2, \ldots, p_n$ are allocated to exactly one of M or N, along with their multiplicities. Since the multiplicities for MN are all even, the same is true for M and N, which are therefore perfect squares. ❑

Theorem 1.10 *If M and N are coprime and a is a factor of MN, then there exist coprime integers b and c such that $a = bc$, where b is a factor of M and c is a factor of N.*

PROOF If the prime factorisation of MN is $p_1^{\alpha_1} p_2^{\alpha_2} \cdots p_n^{\alpha_n}$, then the prime factorisation of a is $p_1^{\beta_1} p_2^{\beta_2} \cdots p_n^{\beta_n}$, for some $0 \leq \beta_i \leq \alpha_i$ for $1 \leq i \leq n$. Each p_i belongs to exactly one of the prime factorisations of M and N, since they are coprime. We now define b and c by dividing $p_1^{\beta_1} p_2^{\beta_2} \cdots p_n^{\beta_n}$ up according to this allocation and the result follows. ❑

We finish the chapter with a famous result known to the Greeks.

Theorem 1.11 (Euclid) *There is an infinite number of primes.*

PROOF Suppose, for contradiction, that this result is false. Thus there would be a maximum prime P. Consider Q, one more than the product of all primes up to and including P, so

$$Q = (2 \times 3 \times 5 \times 7 \times \cdots \times P) + 1.$$

Evidently Q is not divisible by any of $2, 3, 5, 7, \ldots, P$. So either Q is prime or it is divisible only by primes greater than P. In either case we have a contradiction, so there is no maximum prime. ❑

Exercise 1b

1. Factorise into primes 244 578 251 and 944 578 251.

2. Use the method of factorisation into primes to find the highest common factor and the lowest common multiple of 4061 and 3813.

3. If p, q, r are primes and $m = p^2q^3r^4$ and $n = p^4q^2r^3$ find (m, n) and $[m, n]$ and verify that $mn = (m, n) \times [m, n]$.

4. Suppose that the prime factorisation of N is $p_1^{\alpha_1} p_2^{\alpha_2} \cdots p_n^{\alpha_n}$, where $p_1 < p_2 < \cdots < p_n$ and $\alpha_i > 1$. Prove that the number of factors of N is $(\alpha_1 + 1)(\alpha_2 + 1) \cdots (\alpha_n + 1)$.

5. Prove that:

(a) 2 is the only even prime number;

(b) apart from 2 and 3, all prime numbers are of the form $6k - 1$ or $6k + 1$.

6. Prove that there are an infinite number of primes of the form $6k - 1$ (that is, of the form $5, 11, 17, 23, \ldots$).

7. Prove that if p and $p^2 + 2$ are prime then $p^3 + 2$ is also a prime.

8. Prove that for all primes $p > 3$ it is the case that $24 \mid (p^2 - 1)$.

9. What can you say about p if p, $p + 10$ and $p + 14$ are all prime?

10. Prove that if n is odd then $2^n + 1$ is not prime unless $n = 1$.

Project 1 In question 8 of exercise 1a you had lots of 7 g and 4 g weights and in part (b) you should have constructed a table something like table 1.1 on the following page, where $7x + 4y = N$. You should have found that after 17 it looks as though the answer is 'Yes' for all subsequent N. Your first task, if you have not already done it, is to *prove* that all cases with $N > 17$ can be managed.

The abstract project is this: given any two coprime positive integers a and b, find in terms of a and b a formula for the largest positive integer N which *cannot* be expressed in the form $N = xa + yb$, where x and y are non-negative integers. You may suppose without loss of generality that $a > b$. One thing should be pretty obvious and that is the formula must be invariant under exchange of a and b. A fairly simple formula exists and is due to the English mathematician Sylvester who lived in the latter half of the nineteenth century.

N		x	y
0	Yes	0	0
1	No		
2	No		
3	No		
4	Yes	0	1
5	No		
6	No		
7	Yes	1	0
8	Yes	0	2
9	No		
10	No		
11	Yes	1	1
12	Yes	0	3
13	No		
14	Yes	2	0
15	Yes	1	2
16	Yes	0	4
17	No		

Table 1.1

The way to set about such a project is to try other cases besides 7 and 4 for a and b and make sure you keep a catalogue of all the 'Yes' and 'No' cases, as they provide clues for the last part of the project. Try then to guess a formula that satisfies all the evidence you have. But then appreciate your work has only just begun. This is because your formula has to work for all a and b, and not for the few cases you have checked.

In other words there has to be an *algebraic proof* to cover all cases. As mentioned above the formula is fairly easy to discover, but the general proof of why it is correct is hard. You will manage only if you pick up the correct clues from the evidence you have collected. Consider it a success if you make substantial progress.

Chapter 2

Factorisation

2.1 Basic factorisation

Factorisation is the reverse of multiplying out and collecting like terms, so the following factorisations are easily checked:

$$x^2 - y^2 = (x+y)(x-y), \tag{2.1}$$

$$xy + dx + cy + cd = (x+c)(y+d), \tag{2.2}$$

$$abx^2 + (ad+bc)x + cd = (ax+c)(bx+d) \tag{2.3}$$

Of course equation (2.1) is a particular case of equation (2.2), but it is so often used that it is quite rightly the subject of separate exercises in elementary textbooks.

You should make sure you are able to complete the following exercise before proceeding with the text. To factorise an expression such as (2.3) you multiply the coefficient of x^2 and the absolute coefficient to get $abcd$ and then this has to be factored so that the sum of the two factors is $ad + bc$.

Example 2.1 To factorise $6x^2 - xy - 12y^2$.

We have $(ad)(bc) = (ab)(cd) = -72$ and $ad + bc = -1$, and so we can choose $ad = 8$ and $bc = -9$. Combining this with $ab = 6$, $cd = -12$ gives

$$\frac{d}{b} = \frac{4}{3},$$

so setting $b = 3$ gives $a = 2$, $c = -3$ and $d = 4$. Thus the factorisation is $6x^2 - xy - 12y^2 = (2x - 3y)(3x + 4y)$.

Note that the choices for ad and bc are not unique: the point is that we are looking for *integer* values of a, b, c and d, and the process is called *factorisation over the integers*.

Exercise 2a

Factorise the following expressions over the integers.

1. $16x^2 - 25y^2$

2. $200^2 - 1$

3. $16xy - 8x + 4y - 2$

4. $x^4 - y^4$

5. $x^2 + 9x + 14$

6. $x^2 - 9x + 14$

7. $x^2 + 5x - 14$

8. $x^2 - 5x - 14$

9. $6x^2 + 25xy + 14y^2$

10. $12x^2 + xy - 6y^2$

11. $15x^2 - 19xy + 6y^2$

12. $14x^2 - 3xy - 2y^2$

2.2 General factorisation

The expression in example 2.1 has integer coefficients and factorises over the integers. However, not all expressions with integer coefficients can be factorised over the integers, or even over the real numbers.

For example, the expression $x^2 + 2x + 1 - k = (x+1)^2 - k$ factorises over the integers if $k = a^2$, where a is an integer, for then it factorises into $(x+1+a)(x+1-a)$. However, if k is not a perfect square the expression does not factorise over the integers. On the other hand if k is positive, the expression factorises over the real numbers into $(x+1+\sqrt{k})(x+1-\sqrt{k})$. If k is negative the expression no longer factorises over the real numbers, but it factorises over the complex numbers.

A remarkable theorem about complex numbers is that polynomial expressions always factorise into *linear factors* over the complex numbers. The proof is beyond the scope of this book, but the result should be known.

Theorem 2.1 (The fundamental theorem of algebra) *If $a_1, \ldots, a_n$ are any complex numbers there exist complex numbers $b_1, b_2, \ldots, b_n$ such that*

$$z^n + a_1 z^{n-1} + a_2 z^{n-2} + \cdots + a_n = (z-b_1)(z-b_2)\cdots(z-b_n).$$

A corollary of this result is that if the coefficients $a_1, a_2, \ldots, a_n$ are real numbers, then the expression factorises over the real numbers into *linear* and *quadratic* factors. That is, none of the factors need be of degree higher than two. For example,

$$x^3 - y^3 = (x-y)(x^2+xy+y^2),$$
$$x^3 + y^3 = (x+y)(x^2-xy+y^2).$$

There are two remarks which are worth emphasising.

First, not all of these factorisations are factorisations over integers. For example, though

$$x^4 + 4y^4 = \left(x^2+2y^2\right)^2 - 4x^2y^2 = \left(x^2-2xy+2y^2\right)\left(x^2+2xy+2y^2\right),$$

we also have

$$x^4 + y^4 = \left(x^2+y^2\right)^2 - 2x^2y^2 = \left(x^2-\sqrt{2}xy+y^2\right)\left(x^2+\sqrt{2}xy+y^2\right).$$

Secondly, for polynomials with highest power greater than four, we are usually interested in finding a partial factorisation, usually over the integers, rather than a full factorisation. For example, the full factorisation into real factors of $x^5 - 1$ is

$$x^5 - 1 = (x-1)\left(x^2 + \tfrac{1+\sqrt{5}}{2}x + 1\right)\left(x^2 - \tfrac{\sqrt{5}-1}{2}x + 1\right),$$

whereas over the integers, we can produce the partial factorisation

$$x^5 - 1 = (x-1)(x^4 + x^3 + x^2 + x + 1).$$

One use of factorisation is that if an integer can be thrown into an algebraic form that factorises then it cannot be prime (unless one of the factors is 1). For example,

$$973 = 1000 - 27 = 10^3 - 3^3 = (10-3)(10^2 + 10 \times 3 + 3^2) = 7 \times 139.$$

Exercise 2b

1. Factorise over the integers:

(a) 999 991

(b) 9984

(c) 99 999 919.

2. Factorise over the integers:

(a) $x^5 - y^5$

(b) $x^5 + y^5$

(c) $x^4 + 64$

(d) $x^{2k+1} + y^{2k+1}$

(e) $x^{2k+1} - y^{2k+1}$.

3. Factorise 14 640.

4. Factorise 10 064.

5. Prove that no term in the sequence 1001, 1 000 001, 1 000 000 001, ... is prime, where the number of zeros is $3k+2$, $k = 0, 1, 2, \ldots$.

6. Let $N(n) \equiv \frac{1}{3}(4^n - 1)$.

(a) Prove that $N(n)$ is always an integer.

(b) Find the prime factors of $N(4), N(5), N(6)$.

(c) For what values of n does $7 \mid N(n)$?

(d) Prove that if n is not a power of 2 then $N(n)$ has a prime factor of the form $4k+3$ (that is, a prime such as $3, 7, 11, 19 \ldots$).

2.3 Equations of the second degree

Factorisation is a very useful tool in solving problems that lead to algebraic equations. You are no doubt familiar with the solution of quadratic equations by factorisation, but in Number Theory we are more concerned with Diophantine equations, whose solutions are required to be integers.

Example 2.2 To find all positive integers x and y such that

$$x^2 - y^2 = 105.$$

We can frame the problem in factored form $(x+y)(x-y) = 3 \times 5 \times 7$. Now we can see that the following possibilities exist:

$x+y$	$x-y$
105	1
35	3
21	5
15	7

leading to $(x,y) = (53,52)$ or $(19,16)$ or $(13,8)$ or $(11,4)$.

Exercise 2c

1. Find all positive integer values of x and y such that $x^2 - y^2 = 80$.

2. A rectangular chessboard with m rows and n columns has all the squares round the edge cut away. If only two thirds of the squares remain find all possible values of m and n.

3. Find all positive integer values of x and y such that $x^2 - 4y^2 = 80$.

4. Why does the method of example 2.2 not help with trying to find all integer solutions of $x^2 - 2y^2 = 7$?

Project 2 Some factorisations of $2^n + 1$ for different values of n are shown in the table below.

n	$2^n + 1$
3	3×3
4	17
6	5×13
9	$19 \times 3 \times 3 \times 3$
16	65 537
19	$3 \times 174\,763$
24	$97 \times 673 \times 257$

If you have not completed question 10 of exercise 1b you should now be able to do so.

Now investigate what happens when n is even. What do you think might be the case? What can you actually prove? But be careful not to jump to conclusions. There is one hypothesis that is still unproved and I wonder if you can detect what it might be?

Chapter 3

Congruences

3.1 More on divisibility

When an integer is divided by 2, the remainder is either 0 or 1. If the remainder is 0 the integer is said to be *even*, if 1 it is *odd*. Even numbers may be written as $2k$, where k is an integer and odd numbers as $2k+1$. Even squares are therefore of the form $4k^2$ and are divisible by 4. Odd squares, on the other hand, are of the form $4k^2+4k+1 = 4k(k+1)+1$. Now $k(k+1)$ is the product of two consecutive integers and is therefore even. This means that an odd square must be 1 more than a multiple of 8.

From these few remarks we can see that it is useful to divide integers into other categories besides even and odd. What was done for division by 2 can be done for division by 4 or indeed by any other positive integer greater than 1. Just considering the case of 4 for the moment, when an integer is divided by 4 the remainder will be 0, 1, 2 or 3.

A notation has been devised for this. The number whose remainders we are interested in is called the *modulus*, and we indicate this by the phrase '*modulo n*', using also the symbol $\equiv$ rather than $=$.

For instance we write $n \equiv 0 \pmod 4$ if n is divisible by 4, $n \equiv 1 \pmod 4$ if the remainder is 1 after dividing by 4, $n \equiv 2 \pmod 4$ if the remainder is 2 and $n \equiv 3 \pmod 4$ if the remainder is 3.

In this notation an even square is $0 \pmod 4$ and an odd square is $1 \pmod 4$. Indeed an odd square is $1 \pmod 8$.

3.2 Congruences

A statement such as $a \equiv b \pmod{m}$ is called a *congruence*.

It means that the integers a and b both have the same remainder after being divided by the integer m. That is, there exists an integer k such that $a = b + km$ or $m \mid (a - b)$.

Theorem 3.1 *Let a, b, c, d be positive integers and m a positive integer greater than 1. The following statements about congruences are true; the names of the properties are shown in brackets.*

1. $a \equiv a \pmod{m}$. [Reflexive]

2. $a \equiv b \pmod{m} \Leftrightarrow b \equiv a \pmod{m}$. [Symmetric]

3. $a \equiv b \pmod{m}$ *and* $b \equiv c \pmod{m} \Rightarrow a \equiv c \pmod{m}$. [Transitive]

4. $a \equiv b \pmod{m}$ *and* $c \equiv d \pmod{m} \Rightarrow a \pm c = b \pm d \pmod{m}$. [Addition and Subtraction]

5. $a \equiv b \pmod{m}$ *and* $c \equiv d \pmod{m} \Rightarrow ac \equiv bd \pmod{m}$. [Multiplication]

6. $a \equiv b \pmod{m}$ *and* $d \mid m$, *where* $1 < d < m$, $\Rightarrow a \equiv b \pmod{d}$.

7. $a \equiv b \pmod{m}$ *and* $c > 0 \Leftrightarrow ac \equiv bc \pmod{m}$.

Notice that we do not include a statement about division: we have to be careful and the full story will emerge in later chapters.

The proofs of the above are very straightforward and we give only a proof of part 5 to illustrate the method.

PROOF OF PART 5 If $a \equiv b \pmod{m}$ and $c \equiv d \pmod{m}$ there exist integers k, l such that $a = km + b$ and $c = lm + d$. Then

$$ac = (km + b)(lm + d) = (klm + bl + dk)m + bd,$$

showing that $ac \equiv bd \pmod{m}$. ❑

Any set of integers $a_1, a_2, a_3, \ldots, a_m$ such that for every integer x there is one and only one of the a_k such that $x \equiv a_k \pmod{m}$ is called a *complete residue system* modulo m. The most common choice of *residues* is $0, 1, 2, \ldots,$ $(m - 1)$.

It requires a certain amount of practice to handle congruences, so here is a worked example, followed by an exercise.

Example 3.1 We find the solution of $5x \equiv 2 \pmod 7$.

Multiply by 3 to get $15x \equiv 6 \pmod 7$. But $15 \equiv 1 \pmod 7$, so $x \equiv 6 \pmod 7$.

Exercise 3a

1. Prove part 3 of theorem 3.1.

2. Find all values of x satisfying the given congruence:
   (a) $3x \equiv 5 \pmod 7$.
   (b) $6x \equiv 2 \pmod 8$.
   (c) $6x \equiv 1 \pmod 3$.
   (d) $5x \equiv 7 \pmod{11}$.
   (e) $4x \equiv 0 \pmod 6$.

3. If $5x \equiv 5y \pmod{15}$ is it true that $x \equiv y \pmod{15}$?

4. If $5x \equiv 5y \pmod{15}$ is it true that $x \equiv y \pmod 3$?

5. Prove that $2^{12} \equiv 1 \pmod{13}$.

6. Prove that $8x \equiv 8y \pmod{12}$ if, and only if, $x \equiv y \pmod 3$. Can you generalise this?

7. Find the values of x such that $2^x \equiv 1 \pmod 7$.

3.3 Quadratic residues

Example 3.2 We show that $x^2 \equiv 2 \pmod 5$ has no solutions.
The only possibilities are $x \equiv 0, 1, 2, 3, 4 \pmod 5$. The squares of these are $0, 1, 4, 4, 1 \pmod 5$. None of these is 2.

The non-zero values of a such that solutions of $x^2 \equiv a \pmod 5$ exist, that is, $a = 1, 4$, are called the *quadratic residues* (mod 5). In general the values of a coprime to m such that solutions exist of $x^2 \equiv a \pmod m$ are called the *quadratic residues* (mod m). It is worth noting that not all authors have "a coprime to m" in the definition of quadratic residue.

Exercise 3b

1. Find all values of x satisfying the given congruence:
   (a) $x^2 \equiv 2 \pmod 7$.
   (b) $x^2 + x + 1 \equiv 0 \pmod{13}$.

2. Find the quadratic residues (mod 7).

3. Find the quadratic residues (mod 16).

4. Prove that if $n \equiv 2 \pmod 3$ then it cannot be a square.

5. Prove that the sum of two odd squares cannot be a perfect square.

6. Prove that if x, y, z are integers such that $9 \mid (x^2 + y^2 + z^2)$ then $9 \mid (x^2 - y^2)$ or $9 \mid (y^2 - z^2)$ or $9 \mid (z^2 - x^2)$.

7. Find solutions, if any, of the equations:
   (a) $x^2 \equiv -1 \pmod{11}$;
   (b) $x^2 \equiv -1 \pmod{13}$.

   Try a few more primes besides 11 and 13 and make a conjecture from your evidence.

3.4 Tests for divisibility

An integer is divisible by 2 if its last digit is 0, 2, 4, 6, 8. This is because

$$2k \equiv 0,\ 2,\ 4,\ 6,\ 8 \pmod{10},$$

for all integers k. In fact if $k \equiv 0$ or $5 \pmod{10}$, then $2k \equiv 0 \pmod{10}$, if $k \equiv 1$ or $6 \pmod{10}$, then $2k \equiv 2 \pmod{10}$ and so on. Perhaps a better way of looking at this is to say all integers N may be written in the form $N = 10M + R$, where $0 \leq R < 10$, and since 10 is divisible by 2 it follows that $2 \mid N \Leftrightarrow 2 \mid R$.

Example 3.3 The *digital sum* of an integer is the sum of all its digits. We show that an integer is divisible by 9 if and only if its digital sum is divisible by 9.

We write $N = 10M + R$, where $0 \leq R < 10$ and then we have

$$N \equiv M + R \pmod{9}.$$

We now observe that R is the last digit of N. Applying the same method to $M = 10P + S$, where $0 \leq S < 10$, we find

$$N \equiv P + S + R \pmod{9}.$$

We now observe that S is the second last digit of N. Continuing in this way we eventually find that N is equal to its digital sum (mod 9).

One way to devise a test for divisibility by 7 is to use:

Lemma 3.1 $10M + R \equiv 0 \pmod{7}$ *if, and only if,* $M - 2R \equiv 0 \pmod{7}$.

PROOF We have

$$\begin{aligned} & 10M + R \equiv 0 \pmod{7} \\ \Leftrightarrow\quad & 20M + 2R \equiv 0 \pmod{7} \\ \Leftrightarrow\quad & -M + 2R \equiv 0 \pmod{7} \\ \Leftrightarrow\quad & M - 2R \equiv 0 \pmod{7}. \end{aligned}$$

❑

An example should make the method clear. Take the integer 9275. Here $M = 927$ and $R = 5$ and $M - 2R = 917$. Now repeat the process. The new $M = 91$ and the new $R = 7$, then $M - 2R = 77$. Since 77 is obviously divisible by 7 it follows that 9275 is divisible by 7.

A similar method may be used to devise a divisibility test for any prime number. Take for example the prime number 31. We use the result:

Lemma 3.2 $10M + R \equiv 0 \pmod{31}$ *if, and only if,* $M - 3R \equiv 0 \pmod{31}$.

For example, 23 529 leads to $2352 - 27 = 2325$ and this in turn leads to $232 - 15 = 217$. This now leads to $21 - 21 = 0$. Hence 23 529 is divisible by 31.

Exercise 3c

1. State and prove a test for divisibility by
   (a) 4
   (b) 8

2. State and prove a test for divisibility by
   (a) 3
   (b) 11.

3. Prove lemma 3.2.

4. Devise a test for divisibility by
   (a) 17
   (b) 19.

5. Devise a test for divisibility by 47, and illustrate it by showing that 5 802 432 is divisible by 47.

3.5 Pythagorean triples

These are positive integers x, y, z satisfying the equation that occurs in Pythagoras's theorem:

$$x^2 + y^2 = z^2. \tag{3.1}$$

Notice that if d divides any two of x, y, z then it divides the other. Hence, in searching for solutions, we may suppose that x, y, z are mutually coprime (and if required multiply up by a common factor afterwards, corresponding to an integer enlargement of the triangle). This means, in particular, that we may suppose that x, y, z are not all even. Also we know from the result of exercise 3b question 5 that not both of x, y can be odd. This means that one of x, y is even and the other odd, which in turn means that z is odd.

Triples satisfying equation (3.1), without a common factor, are called *primitive Pythagorean triples*; in this book we assume that all Pythagorean triples are primitive. Almost certainly you will have encountered some of the simple cases:

$$3, 4, 5; \quad 5, 12, 13; \quad 8, 15, 17; \quad 7, 24, 25$$

being often used in examination questions.

Project 3 Copy and complete the table below up to $u = 8$ and $v = 7$, and check that in all cases equation (3.1) is satisfied. Here u and v are coprime positive integers of opposite parity (one even and one odd) with $u > v$.

u	v	u^2	v^2	$x = 2uv$	$y = u^2 - v^2$	$z = u^2 + v^2$
2	1	4	1	4	3	5
3	2	9	4	12	5	13
4	1	16	1	8	15	17
4	3	16	9	24	7	25
⋮	⋮	⋮	⋮	⋮	⋮	⋮

A proof that this procedure gives all Pythagorean triples is given in the Solutions and commentary, but, before looking, see if you can prove it. It is the word 'all' that makes it not just a matter of verification that

$$(2uv)^2 + (u^2 - v^2)^2 = (u^2 + v^2)^2.$$

But assuming the formulae are as stated try to prove the following facts:

1. One of x, y must be divisible by 3.
2. One of x, y, z must be divisible by 5.
3. There are an infinite number of cases in which $z = x + 1$.
4. There are an infinite number of cases in which $y = x + 1$.

Finally, find all integer-sided right-angled triangles with a perimeter of 330 units.

Chapter 4

Progressions

4.1 The principle of mathematical induction

In chapter 1 we stated the principle of well-ordering, which is that every non-empty subset of the positive integers has a least member. It was used there to establish the Euclidean algorithm. It also has the immediate consequence that there is no integer between 0 and 1. For suppose such integers exist, then, by the principle, there is a least such integer k and $0 < k < 1$. Multiplying by k we get $0 < k^2 < k < 1$. Since k^2 is an integer less than k we have a contradiction.

The principle of well-ordering also establishes a very powerful method of proof in mathematics, called the principle of mathematical induction.

Theorem 4.1 (The principle of mathematical induction) *Suppose that you are given a sequence of propositions $P(n)$, one such proposition for each integer $n \in \mathbb{N}$, propositions which are either true or false. Then the* principle of mathematical induction *states that if $P(1)$ is true, and if the truth of $P(k)$ implies the truth of $P(k+1)$ for all k, then $P(n)$ is true for all $n \in \mathbb{N}$.*

PROOF Suppose there are some n for which $P(n)$ is not true. Then there is a least such n, say $n = m$. Now $m \neq 1$, since we are given that $P(1)$ is true. Thus $m - 1$ is a positive integer for which $P(m-1)$ is true. Now put $k = m - 1$ and then $P(k+1) = P(m)$ is true. This contradiction establishes the result. ❑

$P(1)$ is sometimes called the *base of the induction*, the assumption that

$P(k)$ is true the *induction hypothesis* and the proof that $P(k)$ implies $P(k+1)$ the *inductive step*.

Example 4.1 We show that $1+2+3+\cdots+n=\frac{1}{2}n(n+1)$.
Call this proposition $P(n)$.
For $n=1$, the left-hand side equals 1 and the right-hand side equals $\frac{1}{2}\times 1\times 2=1$. Hence $P(1)$ is true.
If $P(k)$ is true then $1+2+3+\cdots+k=\frac{1}{2}k(k+1)$ and hence

$$\begin{aligned}1+2+3+\cdots+k+(k+1)&=\tfrac{1}{2}k(k+1)+(k+1)\\&=\tfrac{1}{2}(k+1)(k+2).\end{aligned}$$

Since this is equal to $\frac{1}{2}n(n+1)$ with $n=k+1$, it follows that $P(k+1)$ is true.
And so, by the principle of mathematical induction, $P(n)$ is true for all $n\in\mathbb{N}$.

Example 4.2 We show that $f(n)\equiv 4^{3n-2}+2^{3n-2}+1$ is divisible by 7 for all positive integers n.
Call this proposition $P(n)$.
Now $f(1)=4+2+1=7$ so $P(1)$ is true.
If $P(k)$ is true then there exists an integer m such that

$$f(k)=4^{3k-2}+2^{3k-2}+1=7m.$$

Multiplying by 64 we get

$$4^{3k+1}+2^{3k+4}+64=448m$$

and so

$$\begin{aligned}f(k+1)&=4^{3k+1}+2^{3k+1}+1\\&=448m+2^{3k+1}-2^{3k+4}-63\\&=448m-2^{3k+1}(8-1)-63\\&=7(64m-2^{3k+1}-9).\end{aligned}$$

Since $7 \mid f(k+1)$ it follows that $P(k+1)$ is true.

So, by the principle of mathematical induction, $P(n)$ is true for all $n \in \mathbb{N}$.

The importance of the principle of mathematical induction lies in the fact that it cuts short arguments that would otherwise be of infinite extent and hence not mathematics. The principle is sometimes explained by saying that it validates the sequence of steps $P(1) \Rightarrow P(2) \Rightarrow P(3) \Rightarrow P(4)$ etc. This is unfortunate because the principle of mathematical induction is designed to overcome the problems inherent in such an argument and so the principle must either be proved from the principle of well-ordering or accepted as an axiom. In fact, the axiom of induction and the principle of well-ordering can be shown to be logically equivalent.

The principle of mathematical induction may be extended in ways that also may be proved by the principle of well-ordering.

Theorem 4.2 *Using the same notation, if $P(1)$ and $P(2)$ are true and the truth of $P(k-1)$ and $P(k)$ imply the truth of $P(k+1)$ for all k, then $P(n)$ is true for all $n \in \mathbb{N}$.*

Example 4.3 We show that if (u_n) is a sequence such that $u_1 = 1$, $u_2 = 5$ and $u_{n+1} = 5u_n - 6u_{n-1}$ for $n \geq 2$, then $u_n = 3^n - 2^n$.

$P(1)$ is true since $3 - 2 = 1$ and $P(2)$ is true since $9 - 4 = 5$.

If $P(k-1)$ and $P(k)$ are true then $u_{k-1} = 3^{k-1} - 2^{k-1}$ and $u_k = 3^k - 2^k$ and from the recurrence relation we have

$$\begin{aligned} u_{k+1} &= 5 \times 3^k - 5 \times 2^k - 6 \times 3^{k-1} + 6 \times 2^{k-1} \\ &= 3^{k-1}(15 - 6) + 2^{k-1}(6 - 10) \\ &= 3^{k+1} - 2^{k+1} \end{aligned}$$

and hence $P(k+1)$ is true.

It follows that $P(n)$ is true for all $n \in \mathbb{N}$.

The following theorem is referred to as the *second* or *strong* principle of mathematical induction.

Theorem 4.3 *Using the same notation, if $P(1)$ is true and the truth of all $P(n)$ for $n = 1, 2, 3, \ldots, k$ imply the truth of $P(k+1)$, then $P(n)$ is true for all $n \in \mathbb{N}$.*

It should also be noted that there is no reason why the start of an induction should be the case $n = 1$. If the start is $n = 3$, for example, then an induction only proves $P(n)$ to be true for integers $n \geq 3$. Quite often it is convenient to start at $n = 0$.

Exercise 4a

The following questions should be answered using the principle of mathematical induction.

1. Prove that $1^2 + 2^2 + 3^2 + \cdots + n^2 = \frac{1}{6}n(n+1)(2n+1)$.

2. Prove that

$$\frac{1}{1 \times 2} + \frac{1}{2 \times 3} + \frac{1}{3 \times 4} + \cdots + \frac{1}{n(n+1)} = \frac{n}{n+1}.$$

3. Prove that $n^3 - 25n$ is divisible by 6 for all positive integers n .

4. Consider the sequence (u_n) defined by $u_1 = 3$, $u_2 = 5$ and

$$u_{n+2} = 3u_{n+1} - 2u_n,\ n \geq 1.$$

   Make a conjecture about the value of u_n and establish its truth by induction.

4.2 Arithmetic progressions

The word 'progression' in this context has been used for a long time, but only means the same as the word 'sequence'. An *arithmetic progression* is defined as the sequence (u_n) such that $u_1 = a$, $u_2 = a + d$, $u_3 = a + 2d, \ldots,$

$u_n = a + (n-1)d$, where a and d are constants. The *first term* is a and since the difference between any two consecutive terms is constant and equal to d it is called the *common difference*.

It is very easy to find the sum of an arithmetic series

$$\begin{aligned} u_1 + u_2 + u_3 + \cdots + u_n &= a + (a+d) + (a+2d) + \cdots (a + (n-1)d) \\ &= na + d[1 + 2 + \cdots + (n-1)] \\ &= na + \tfrac{1}{2}n(n-1)d \\ &= \tfrac{1}{2}n[2a + (n-1)d], \end{aligned}$$

where we have used the result of example 4.1. This can also be written as $\frac{1}{2}n(a+l)$, where l is the last term.

As an example,

$$17 + 21 + 25 + \cdots + 221 = 26(34 + 51 \times 4) = 6188,$$

since $a = 17, d = 4$ and $n = 52$.
Note that

$$u_n = \tfrac{1}{2}(u_{n-1} + u_{n+1}),$$

so that each term is the *arithmetic mean* of the terms on either side of it.

Exercise 4b

1. Find the sum of the first 50 odd integers.

2. Locate all the terms in the following two arithmetic progressions that are equal:

$$13,\ 18,\ 23,\ 28,\ \ldots \quad \text{and} \quad 7,\ 13,\ 19,\ 25,\ \ldots$$

3. Find the sum of all the natural numbers between 1 and 3000 inclusive that are not divisible by 2 or 3.

4. Characterise those positive integers that can be represented as the sum of two or more consecutive positive integers.

5. Find the least value of n such that

$$105 + 109 + 113 + \cdots + (101 + 4n) > 1\,000\,000.$$

4.3 Geometric progressions

A *geometric progression* is defined as a sequence (u_n) such that $u_1 = a$, $u_2 = ar$, $u_3 = ar^2, \ldots, u_n = ar^{n-1}$, where a and r are constants. The *first term* is a and since the quotient of any two consecutive terms is constant and equal to r it is called the *common ratio*. The sum of a geometric progression may be obtained as follows:

Consider the factorisation

$$x^n - 1 = (x-1)(x^{n-1} + x^{n-2} + \cdots + x + 1).$$

This may be recast in the form

$$1 + x + x^2 + \cdots + x^{n-1} = \frac{x^n - 1}{x - 1}, \quad x \neq 1.$$

When $x < 1$, it is more convenient to rewrite the right-hand side as $\frac{1-x^n}{1-x}$. It follows that the sum of the first n terms of a geometric progression is

$$\begin{aligned} a + ar + ar^2 + \cdots + ar^{n-1} &= a(1 + r + r^2 + \cdots + r^{n-1}) \\ &= a\frac{r^n - 1}{r - 1}, \quad r \neq 1. \end{aligned}$$

As an example,

$$3 + 6 + 12 + 24 + \ldots + 3 \times 2^{49} = 3\frac{2^{50} - 1}{2 - 1} = 3(2^{50} - 1),$$

since $a = 3, r = 2$ and $n = 50$.

Note that if all terms of a geometric progression are positive then

$$u_n = \sqrt{u_{n-1}u_{n+1}}$$

so that each term is the *geometric mean* of the two terms on either side of it.

Exercise 4c

1. Find the sum of $5 + 30 + 180 + 1080 + \cdots + 5 \times 6^{19}$.

2. Find the sum of $9 - 3 + 1 - \frac{1}{3} + \frac{1}{9} + \cdots$ to 13 terms. To what value does the sum approach as the number of terms increases?

3. Prove that the geometric mean of two positive numbers is less than or equal to their arithmetic mean.

4. What is the least value of n such that $1 + 5 + 25 + \cdots + 5^{n-1} > 1\,000\,000$?

Project 4 The divisors of 6 are 1, 2, 3, 6. They are four in number and their sum is 12. We shall write $d(n)$ for *the number of divisors of* n and $\sigma(n)$ for *their sum*. Such functions defined on the positive integers are called *arithmetic functions*.

It turns out to be possible to calculate the values of $d(n)$ and $\sigma(n)$ without listing the divisors. For example, $d(200) = 12$ and $\sigma(200) = 465$. The project is to find out how to do it, with just a little bit of preliminary help.

First a few results; you should check them and add a few of your own.

n	$d(n)$	$\sigma(n)$
5	2	6
6	4	12
7	2	8
8	4	15
9	3	13
49	3	57
63	6	104
72	12	195
100	9	217

Here are a few things to think about.

- If p is prime what are $d(p)$ and $\sigma(p)$?
- If $n = p^2$, where p is prime, then what are $d(n)$ and $\sigma(n)$?
- What can you say about n when $d(n)$ is odd?

Make sure that you prove your assertions and do not be satisfied with guesses which appear to fit the data.

- What happens if $n = p^3$, where p is prime?

Suppose now both p and q are prime.

- What happens if $n = pq$?
- What happens if $n = pq^2$ or $n = p^2q^2$?
- What happens if $n = p^kq^m$?

A hint is that you are not on the right track unless you are summing geometrical progressions when working out $\sigma(n)$.

Now try the following:

1. Find the smallest positive integer n for which $d(n) = 6$.
2. Find a necessary and sufficient condition on n for $\sigma(n)$ to be odd.
3. The integer m is said to be a *perfect number* if $\sigma(m) = 2m$. For example, 6 is a perfect number since $\sigma(6) = 12$. There is another perfect number less than 30. Find it.
4. Prove that if $2^n - 1 = p$ is prime then $2^{n-1}p$ is perfect.

Chapter 5

Sums of squares

5.1 Perfect squares

We have already covered enough theory for you to be able to manage the first exercise, and it is suggested that you try these problems before we embark on some new ideas and techniques.

Exercise 5a

1. The four-digit integer '*aabb*' is a square. Find a and b.

2. Prove that the sum of the squares of five successive positive integers is never a square.

3. The triangular number T_n is defined as $\frac{1}{2}n(n+1)$ for $n = 1, 2, 3, \ldots$. Show how to find all values for which T_n is a perfect square and find the first four such triangular numbers.

5.2 Sums of squares

We now investigate which positive integers can be written as the sum of two squares, and the number of different ways in which this can be done.

Note that we do not deem $p^2 + q^2$ and $q^2 + p^2$ to be different expressions in this context.

There is a very useful algebraic identity:

$$(ax + by)^2 + (ay - bx)^2 = (a^2 + b^2)(x^2 + y^2). \tag{5.1}$$

For example, putting $a = 3$, $b = 2$, $x = 5$, $y = 9$ in identity (5.1) gives

$$33^2 + 17^2 = (3^2 + 2^2)(5^2 + 9^2).$$

Replacing y by $-y$ yields the sister identity:

$$(ax - by)^2 + (ay + bx)^2 = (a^2 + b^2)(x^2 + y^2). \tag{5.2}$$

Exercise 5b

1. Consider the following:

$$\begin{aligned} 3^2 + 4^2 &= 25, & 7^2 + 1^2 &= 50, \\ 4^2 + 6^2 &= 52, & 10^2 + 2^2 &= 104, \\ 5^2 + 9^2 &= 106, & 14^2 + 4^2 &= 212. \end{aligned}$$

Prove that if the integer n is the sum of two squares then $2n$ is also.

2. Express 1378 as the sum of two squares in two different ways.

3. What is the smallest integer that can be expressed as the sum of two squares in two different ways?

4. Now put $a = 5$, $b = 6$, $x = 12$, $y = 10$ and construct similar numerical results to those for $a = 3$, $b = 2$, $x = 5$, $y = 9$.

5. Which of the primes between 5 and 97 inclusive can be expressed as the sum of two perfect squares, and in how many different ways?

6. Prove that no prime of the form 3 (mod 4) is expressible as the sum of two perfect squares.

7. Let p_1, p_2, p_3 be distinct primes which can be expressed as the sum of two positive integer squares. In how many different ways can $p_1p_2p_3$ be expressed as the sum of two positive integer squares?

Theorem 5.1 *Let $S(2)$ be the set of all integers that can be expressed as the sum of two squares (including the case when one of those squares is 0). If $g \in S(2)$ and $h \in S(2)$, then $gh \in S(2)$.*

PROOF This follows immediately from identity (5.1) or (5.2). ❑

Theorem 5.1 gives an example of what is known in mathematics as a *closure property*. We say that the set $S(2)$ is closed under multiplication. The positive integers are closed under multiplication and they have the property that they are all expressible as multiples of 1 and the positive primes. As we see shortly the same sort of things happen with the set $S(2)$.

Theorem 5.2 *The following and only the following integers belong to $S(2)$, and can be expressed as the sum of two perfect squares (one of which may be zero):*

$$2^k pq \dots s u^2 v^2 \dots x^2,$$

where k is a non-negative integer, $p, q, \dots, s$ are primes of the form $1 \pmod 4$ and $u, v, \dots, x$ are primes of the form $3 \pmod 4$. In this expression some primes may be repeated, and there may be no prime of either one form or the other.

PROOF Most of this follows from the results so far. In view of the closure property the only part of this theorem unproved is that odd primes of the form $1 \pmod 4$ are all uniquely expressible as the sum of two positive integer squares. For a proof of this, see [2]. You may use this result. ❑

5.3 The triangular numbers

These are $1, 3, 6, 10, 15, \dots$. The nth triangular number is

$$T_n = \tfrac{1}{2}n(n+1).$$

They are closely related to the squares in view of the fact that

$$8T_n + 1 = (2n+1)^2.$$

Although in general it is difficult to say how mathematicians of previous ages compare with the best of those today, it is safe to say that Gauss was one of the greatest mathematicians who ever lived. Like Archimedes he used the word *Eureka* (in large letters on a manuscript) when he proved

Theorem 5.3 (Gauss's eureka) *All positive integers are expressible as the sum of no more than three triangular numbers.*

Unfortunately this is another result that we do not prove in this book. The proof is set as a problem in [2].

Exercise 5c

1. Prove that

$$4(T_m + T_n) + 1 = (m + n + 1)^2 + (m - n)^2. \quad (5.3)$$

2. Show that any number of the form $a^2 + b^2 + b$, where a, b are positive integers, can be written as the sum of two triangular numbers.

3. Use Gauss's Eureka to prove that all positive integers of the form $3 \pmod 8$ are expressible as the sum of three perfect squares.

4. Prove that all integers of the form $7 \pmod 8$ are expressible as the sum of four squares.

5. Identity (5.3) may remind you of the characterisation of Pythagorean triples in project 3 on page 27:

$$(2uv)^2 + (u^2 - v^2)^2 = (u^2 + v^2)^2.$$

   (a) Suppose, first, that the left-hand side of identity (5.3) is an odd perfect square, say $(4k + 1)^2$. Show that this implies that

$$T_m + T_n = 2T_{2k}.$$

   (b) We would therefore like to find u, v such that

$$\begin{aligned} 2uv &= m - n \\ u^2 - v^2 &= m + n + 1 \\ u^2 + v^2 &= 4k + 1 \end{aligned}$$

for appropriate values of m, n and k. Defining $u = a + b + 1$, $v = a - b$ for positive integers a, b with $a > b$, find m, n and k in terms of a, b which would achieve this. Show that k is the sum of two triangular numbers.

(c) By taking $a = 13$, $b = 10$ find the appropriate Pythagorean triple and two triangular numbers whose arithmetic mean is another triangular number.

Project 5 *Gaussian integers* are expressions of the form $z = x + iy$ where x and y are integers and $i^2 = -1$. Apart from that, they obey the usual rules of algebra. The complex conjugate of z is defined as $z^* = x - iy$. It is easy to show that $zz^* = x^2 + y^2$, and that $(zw)^* = z^* w^*$ for two complex numbers z and w.

1. By taking $z = x + iy$ and $w = a + ib$, derive the identities (5.1) and (5.2) on page 38.

It is possible to derive similar results for sums of four squares using numbers known as *quaternion integers*. These are expressions of the form

$$aE + uI + vJ + wK,$$

where a, u, v, w are integers and E, I, J, K are the quaternion units satisfying

$$\begin{aligned} &E^2 = E, \quad I^2 = J^2 = K^2 = -E, \\ &IJ = -JI = K, \quad JK = -KJ = I, \quad KI = -IK = J \\ \text{and} \quad &EI = I = IE, \quad EJ = J = JE, \quad EK = K = KE. \end{aligned}$$

2. Prove that if

$$\begin{aligned} P &= aE + uI + vJ + wK \\ \text{and} \quad P^* &= aE - uI - vJ - wK, \end{aligned}$$

then

$$PP^* = a^2 + u^2 + v^2 + w^2.$$

3. Now let

$$P = aE + uI + vJ + wK$$
$$Q = bE + xI + yJ + zK$$

be two quaternion integers. By proving that

$$(PQ)(PQ)^* = (PP^*)(QQ^*)$$

show that an integer which is represented by the sum of four integer squares multiplied by another such integer is equal to an integer that is itself represented by the sum of four integer squares.

Chapter 6

Fermat's little theorem

6.1 Arithmetic modulo an odd prime

Exercise 6a

1. Copy and complete the following multiplication tables.

   (a) Modulo 5:

$\times$	1	2	3	4
1	1	2	3	4
2	2	4	1	3
3				
4				

   (b) Modulo 7:

$\times$	1	2	3	4	5	6
1	1	2				
2	2	4	6	1	3	
3						
4						
5						
6						

(c) Modulo 11:

×	1	2	3	4	5	6	7	8	9	10
1										
2										
3										
4										
5										
6										
7	7	3	10	6	2	9	5	1	8	4
8										
9										
10										

2. What do you notice in each case about the array of answers?

3. For each value of m, $m = 1$ to 4, work out the smallest positive value of n such that $m^n \equiv 1 \pmod 5$.

4. For each value of m, $m = 1$ to 6, work out the smallest positive value of n such that $m^n \equiv 1 \pmod 7$.

5. For each value of m, $m = 1$ to 10, work out the smallest positive value of n such that $m^n \equiv 1 \pmod{11}$.

Theorem 6.1 *If p is an odd prime and $(a, p) = 1$, then*

$$a,\ 2a,\ 3a,\ \ldots,\ (p-1)a \ (\text{mod } p)$$

is a rearrangement of the integers

$$1,\ 2,\ 3,\ \ldots,\ p-1.$$

PROOF Since $(a, p) = 1$ none of a, $2a$, …, $(p-1)a$ is $0 \pmod p$, so the theorem is true provided no two are equal $(\text{mod } p)$. Suppose, in fact, that $ma \equiv na \pmod p$, then $(m-n)a \equiv 0 \pmod p$. Since $(a, p) = 1$ it follows that $m \equiv n \pmod p$. But $0 < m, n < p$ and hence $m = n$. It follows that the integers are all different and are therefore a rearrangement of 1, 2, 3, …, $p-1$. ❑

Corollary 6.1 *It follows that for every* $a \in \{1, 2, 3, \ldots, p-1\}$ *there exists a unique partner* b *such that* $ab = ba \equiv 1 \pmod{p}$.

The partner is called the *inverse* of a and is sometimes written as a^{-1}.

The set $\mathbb{Z}_p = \{0, 1, 2, 3, \ldots, p-1\}$ under the operations $+ \bmod p$ and $\times \bmod p$ is what is known algebraically as a *finite field*, which basically means that the ordinary rules of arithmetic are valid, and in particular you can divide by any non-zero number, with the convention that $\frac{m}{a}$ is defined to be $a^{-1}m \pmod{p}$. For those familiar with the terminology, $\mathbb{Z}_p$ is a *cyclic group* of order p under $+ \bmod p$ and $\mathbb{Z}_p \backslash \{0\}$ is an *abelian group* of order $p-1$ under $\times \bmod p$.

Theorem 6.2 (Fermat's little theorem) *Let* p *be an odd prime. If* $(a, p) = 1$, *then*

$$a^{p-1} \equiv 1 \pmod{p}. \tag{6.1}$$

and for every integer m

$$m^p \equiv m \pmod{p}. \tag{6.2}$$

PROOF 1 We know from theorem 6.1 that if $(a, p) = 1$, then

$$(1a)(2a)(3a) \cdots ((p-1)a) \equiv (1)(2)(3) \cdots (p-1) \pmod{p},$$

and since $(p-1)!$ is coprime to p we may cancel it from both sides leaving equation (6.1). Equation (6.2) is immediate once (6.1) is proved. ❑

For those familiar with finite group theory we give another argument.

PROOF 2 For any element $a \in \mathbb{Z}_p \backslash \{0\}$ let n be the smallest positive integer such that $a^n \equiv 1 \pmod{p}$. Then $\{1, a, a^2, \ldots, a^{n-1}\}$ forms a cyclic subgroup with n elements in the entire group, which is of order $p-1$, so, by Lagrange's theorem, $p - 1 = kn$ and so $a^{p-1} = a^{kn} = (a^n)^k \equiv 1^k = 1 \pmod{p}$. ❑

Finally we give a third way to demonstrate this important result.

PROOF 3 In this proof you need to know what is meant by a *cyclic permutation*. It is very simple: for example, the cyclic permutations of *abcde* are *abcde*, *bcdea*, *cdeab*, *deabc*, *eabcd* and are five in number.

Suppose we have a lot of beads of m different colours. Out of these we are going to make necklaces with exactly p beads, considering them to be viewed from one side only, as if a person is wearing them. First we make a string of beads with p beads. Since there are m colours the first bead can be any of m colours and likewise the second and so on. There are therefore m^p different strings of beads. From these we remove the m strings in which all the beads are of the same colour. This leaves $m^p - m$ strings. We now join up the ends of the strings to form necklaces. Two strings that differ only by having a different cyclic permutation of the same set of beads form indistinguishable necklaces. Since there are p cyclic permutations of p beads on a string, the number of distinct necklaces is

$$\frac{m^p - m}{p}.$$

Because of its meaning this must be an integer. Equation (6.2) follows.

Now, if $(a, p) = 1$, we have $a^p \equiv a \pmod{p}$ and now we can divide both sides by a to obtain equation (6.1). ❑

This type of proof is called a *combinatorial proof*, because it relies on an argument involving counting. Alternatively it can be called a *bijective proof*, because it involves setting up a 1-1 correspondence with a set which can be counted. Such proofs need considerable care, for as they can be rather verbal in character they can be misleading, as shown in question 1 of exercise 6b on page 48.

Those unfamiliar with group theory should still be made familiar with what is meant by the order of an element $\pmod{p}$. It was the aim of questions 3, 4 and 5 in exercise 6a on page 44 to give numerical evidence of what the order of an element is and what is its main property. If $(a, p) = 1$ and p is an odd prime, then the *order* of $a \pmod{p}$ is the smallest positive integer n such that $a^n \equiv 1 \pmod{p}$.

Theorem 6.3 *The order of $a \pmod{p}$ divides $p - 1$.*

PROOF Let n be the order of a and suppose n does not divide $p - 1$, then $p - 1 = qn + r$, where, by the Euclidean algorithm studied in chapter 1, $0 < r < n$. Then, by theorem 6.2, we have

$$1 = a^{p-1} = a^{qn+r} = (a^n)^q a^r = a^r,$$

since $a^n = 1$, by definition. But this contradicts the definition that n is the *smallest* positive integer such that $a^n = 1$. It follows that $n \mid (p - 1)$. ❑

Fermat's little theorem can be used to show that an integer is not prime. For example, $2^{64} \equiv 16 \not\equiv 1 \pmod{65}$ and hence 65 is not prime. Of course, there are easier ways of showing that 65 is not prime, but when dealing with very large numbers it is possible by such means to show that an integer is composite without knowing any of its prime factors. Fermat's little theorem deals with large numbers as efficiently as it deals with small numbers, as the following examples show.

Example 6.1 We work out $7^{44} \pmod{13}$.

From theorem 6.2

$$7^{12} \equiv 1 \pmod{13}.$$

Hence

$$7^{36} \equiv 1 \pmod{13}.$$

So

$$7^{44} \equiv 7^8 \pmod{13}.$$

Now

$$7^2 \equiv 10 \pmod{13},$$

so

$$7^4 \equiv 100 \equiv 9 \pmod{13}$$

and

$$7^8 \equiv 81 \equiv 3 \pmod{13}.$$

Example 6.2 We solve the congruence $x^{15} \equiv 48 \pmod{59}$.

We have

$$x^{30} \equiv 48^2 \equiv 3 \pmod{59}$$

so

$$x^{60} \equiv 9 \pmod{59}.$$

But by theorem 6.2

$$x^{58} \equiv 1 \pmod{59},$$

so we have

$$x^2 \equiv 9 \pmod{59}$$

leading to

$$x \equiv 3 \text{ or } 56 \pmod{59}.$$

Example 6.3 We investigate whether there are any solutions of the congruence $x^3 \equiv 5 \pmod{13}$.

If there were then $x^6 \equiv 25 \equiv -1 \pmod{13}$ and $x^{12} \equiv 1 \pmod{13}$, which is compatible with theorem 6.2. It is now worth seeking the solutions.

The cubes of $1, 2, 3, \ldots, 12 \pmod{13}$ are $1, 8, 1, 12, 8, 8, 5, 5, 1, 12, 5, 12$. So the solutions are $x \equiv 7, 8, 11 \pmod{13}$.

Exercise 6b

1. Where does Proof 3 on page 45 go wrong when p is not prime?

2. Use Fermat's little theorem to show that 16 637 is not prime.

3. Solve $x^{97} \equiv 5 \pmod{11}$.

4. Find an integer $0 < x < 59$ such that $x \equiv 9^{50} \pmod{59}$.

6.2 Pseudoprimes and Carmichael numbers

The converse of Fermat's little theorem is not true. The counterexample with the least exponent is 340, since $2^{340} \equiv 1 \pmod{341}$. In fact $2^5 \equiv 1 \pmod{31}$ and $2^{10} \equiv 1 \pmod{11}$. Hence $2^{340} \equiv 1 \pmod{31}$ and $2^{340} \equiv 1 \pmod{11}$ and so $2^{340} \equiv 1 \pmod{341}$. We say that 341 is a *pseudoprime* to the base 2. There is an infinite number of pseudoprimes to the base 2, or indeed to any base. So Fermat's little theorem cannot definitely establish that an integer is prime, but it may suggest that a number is prime.

In theorem 6.3 it is proved that the order of an element $\pmod{p}$, where p is an odd prime, divides $p-1$. It has not been shown here that an element exists which actually has order $p-1$. If such an element exists it is called a *primitive root* modulo p. In fact such elements do exist, which means that the group $\mathbb{Z}_p \backslash \{0\}$ is cyclic. The number of distinct primitive roots is also known. We do not establish these results in this book.

A composite integer m such that $a^m \equiv a \pmod{m}$ for every integer a such that $1 \leq a \leq m$ is called a *Carmichael number*. The first four Carmichael numbers are 561, 1105, 1729, and 2465. It was only proved in 1984 that there are an infinite number of Carmichael numbers, a conjecture originally made by Carmichael himself in 1910.

Exercise 6c

1. Work out $4! \pmod{5}$, $6! \pmod{7}$ and $10! \pmod{11}$, decide on a probable theorem and prove it.

2. For p an odd prime factorise $x^{p-1} - 1 \pmod{p}$.

3. Prove that 561 is a Carmichael number.

Project 6 Recall from section 3.2 on page 22 that the numbers $1, 2, 3, \ldots, p-1$, where p is prime, form a complete residue system $\pmod{p}$. Any set of $p-1$ integers congruent to them also forms a complete set.

The numbers $1^2, 2^2, 3^2, \ldots, (p-1)^2 \pmod{p}$ are quadratic residues $\pmod{p}$: recall section 3.3 on page 24. In the project that follows you may assume the existence of primitive roots modulo p where p is an odd prime.

1. Prove that 1, 2, 4 are the distinct quadratic residues $\pmod{7}$.
2. Work out the distinct quadratic residues modulo 11, 13, 17 and 19.
3. How many quadratic residues are there $\pmod{p}$, where p is an odd prime? Justify your answer.
4. For which primes p is -1 a quadratic residue? Prove your assertion.
5. Find the solutions of the congruence $x^2 + 8x + 14 \equiv 0 \pmod{23}$.

Chapter 7

Euler's totient function

7.1 The function $\phi(x)$

We now generalise the work of chapter 6 to include congruences modulo m, where m is not necessarily prime. We observe that the congruence $a^k \equiv 1 \pmod{m}$ can only hold if a and m are coprime. For if this equation is true, then there exists an integer n such that $a^k - nm = 1$. Hence, if $(a, m) = h$ we have $h \mid a^k - nm$, that is $h \mid 1$ and so $h = 1$. It is natural therefore, for a positive integer m, to consider the set

$$\{a : 1 \leq a < m,\ (a, m) = 1\},$$

that is, the set of positive integers less than m that are coprime to m.

The standard notation for the number of elements in this set is $\phi(m)$. Thus $\phi(6) = 2$, since out of 1, 2, 3, 4, 5 only 1 and 5 are coprime to 6. The function ϕ is called *Euler's totient function* (or sometimes *Euler's ϕ-function*).

Exercise 7a

1. Show that $\phi(8) = 4$ and evaluate $\phi(m)$ for $m = 1$ to 12.

2. Work out $\phi(p)$, where p is prime.

3. Prove that $\phi(p^2) = p(p-1)$, where p is prime.

4. Make a list of the positive integers less than 18 that are coprime to 18, and hence show that $\phi(18) = 6$. For each of these positive integers a work out $a^6 \pmod{18}$.

Fermat's little theorem and results such as those in question 4 of exercise 7a suggest the following generalisation of Fermat's little theorem.

Theorem 7.1 (Euler-Fermat) *If a is any positive integer coprime to m, then*

$$a^{\phi(m)} \equiv 1 \pmod{m}.$$

PROOF Suppose the distinct residues (mod m) that are coprime to m are denoted by $c_1, c_2, c_3, \ldots, c_{\phi(m)}$ and a is any element of this set. Then we claim that $ac_1, ac_2, ac_3, \ldots, ac_{\phi(m)} \pmod{m}$ are distinct, for if not, suppose $ac_j = ac_k \pmod{m}$, with $j \neq k$, then $a(c_j - c_k) \equiv 0 \pmod{m}$. But $(a, m) = 1$, so $c_j \equiv c_k \pmod{m}$. But each c_k lies between 1 and $(m-1)$ inclusive, and hence $c_j = c_k$. Contradiction establishes the result. This means that $ac_1, ac_2, ac_3, \ldots, ac_{\phi(m)} \pmod{m}$ is simply a rearrangement of the residues, so their products are equal. Cancelling out the common expression $c_1c_2c_3 \cdots c_{\phi(m)}$ which is allowable, since each of the terms in the product is coprime to m, we are left with the required result $a^{\phi(m)} \equiv 1 \pmod{m}$. ❑

The proof follows exactly the same steps as in proof 1 of Fermat's little theorem (page 45). The *order* of a is defined, as before as the least positive integer n, such that $a^n \equiv 1 \pmod{m}$. And it follows exactly as in theorem 6.3 that $n \mid \phi(m)$. From theorem 7.1 it follows that every element a coprime to m has an inverse b also coprime to m such that $ab = ba \equiv 1 \pmod{m}$. If we denote the set $\{c_1, c_2, c_3, \ldots, c_{\phi(m)}\}$ by G_m, then G_m is an Abelian group under $\times$ mod m. We stated in chapter 6 that $G_p = \mathbb{Z}_p \backslash \{0\}$, when p is prime, is a cyclic group, so that there exists a primitive root. It can be proved that a residue coprime to m exists with order $\phi(m)$ if and only if m takes on any of the values 1, 2, 4, p^k, $2p^k$, where p is any odd prime and k is any positive integer. Such a residue is called a *primitive root* modulo m. We do not give the proof in this book, but one may be found in [2]. In other cases G_m may be far from cyclic: see, for example, G_{24} in question 2 of exercise 7b.

Exercise 7b

1. Find the value of $\phi(25)$ and find a primitive root modulo 25.

2. (a) List all the elements of G_{24}.

   (b) Produce a square multiplication table (mod 24) for the products of all the elements of G_{24}.

   (c) What is the smallest integer n such that $11^n \equiv 1 \pmod{24}$? Are there any elements of order 4?

3. What is the analogue of Wilson's theorem (page 161) concerning the value of the product $M = c_1c_2c_3 \cdots c_{\phi(m)}$?

7.2 The Chinese remainder theorem

If you are set an exercise such as the following: 'Find a positive integer that has a remainder 1 when divided by 2, a remainder of 2 when divided by 3 and a remainder of 3 when divided by 5', then it is easy to solve mentally. First you note that the integer is odd, then you might say that to be of the form $3t + 2$, it is possibly 5, 11, 17, 23, ... Finally you might observe that 23 satisfies the conditions of the problem. If you were then asked to find some more integers with the same property, you would guess that as odd numbers repeat with a period of 2, multiples of three with a period of 3 and multiples of five with a period of 5 then you would have to jump ahead by multiples of $2 \times 3 \times 5 = 30$, and hence that the general solution is probably $23 \pmod{30}$.

Whilst such questions are straightforward when the numbers involved are small and the number of conditions imposed are few, they are less so for large numbers or when more conditions are involved. Also there is the question of how sure we are of getting all the solutions by a method that is not dependent on some general theory, and how do we know whether the conditions imposed are self-contradictory.

Theorem 7.2 (Chinese remainder theorem) *Suppose that m and n are two coprime integers, then the equations*

$$\begin{aligned} x &\equiv a \pmod{m} \\ \textit{and} \quad x &\equiv b \pmod{n} \end{aligned}$$

have common solution $x = x_0$ *and the full set of solutions consists of those* x *of the form* $x \equiv x_0 \pmod{mn}$.

Clearly if two simultaneous congruences with respect to coprime moduli have a solution, then any finite number of simultaneous congruences with respect to mutually coprime moduli have a solution. This is because one can solve the first two, then from their solution and the third congruence one may obtain a solution by the same process and so on. The proof of the theorem provides a constructive method of solution, though in applications it is usually the mere existence of a solution that is required.

PROOF Since m and n are coprime there exist integers c and d such that $cn \equiv 1 \pmod{m}$ and $dm \equiv 1 \pmod{n}$. Furthermore $cn \equiv 0 \pmod{n}$ and $dm \equiv 0 \pmod{m}$. We now form the integer $x_0 = acn + bdm$, and observe it provides one solution to the problem. Now any two solutions must have a difference that is $0 \pmod{m}$ and $0 \pmod{n}$ and, since m and n are coprime, it follows that the second solution differs from the first by some multiple of mn. ❑

The theorem is called the Chinese remainder theorem since it appears in a book from the third century AD by the mathematician Sun Zi.

Example 7.1 Let us see how it works for the pair

$$x \equiv 7 \pmod{8}$$
$$\text{and} \quad x \equiv 3 \pmod{5}.$$

We have $a = 7$, $b = 3$, $m = 8$, $n = 5$. We have $5 \times 5 \equiv 1 \pmod{8}$ so $c = 5$ and $2 \times 8 \equiv 1 \pmod{5}$ so $d = 2$. We then form

$$x_0 = 7 \times 5 \times 5 + 3 \times 2 \times 8 \equiv 175 + 48 = 223 \pmod{40}.$$

More simply $x \equiv 23 \pmod{40}$ is the general solution.

Exercise 7c

1. Use the method described in the first paragraph of section 7.2 on the previous page to find positive integers that have a remainder 5 when divided by 7 and a remainder of 6 when divided by 9.

2. Find the smallest positive integer that gives remainders 1, 2, 3, 4 when divided by 3, 5, 7, 11 respectively.

3. Solve the equations

$$\begin{aligned} 6x &\equiv 9 \pmod{15} \\ \text{and} \quad 3x &\equiv 17 \pmod{44} \end{aligned}$$

first as separate equations, and then as a simultaneous pair.

That m, n should be mutually coprime is a sufficient condition for solutions to exist, but it is not necessary. For example,

$$\begin{aligned} x &\equiv 3 \pmod{5} \\ \text{and} \quad x &\equiv 8 \pmod{10} \end{aligned}$$

obviously have solutions. But

$$\begin{aligned} x &\equiv 3 \pmod{5} \\ \text{and} \quad x &\equiv 1 \pmod{10} \end{aligned}$$

obviously do not. They are said to be *inconsistent*.

7.3 Multiplicative functions

The idea of an arithmetic function was introduced in project 4 on page 35. These are functions defined on the positive integers. We now introduce a very important concept in the theory of numbers, that of a multiplicative function. A *multiplicative function* is an arithmetic function f with the property that $f(mn) = f(m)f(n)$ whenever m and n are coprime.

Exercise 7d

1. Work out $\phi(15)$ and show it is equal to $\phi(5)\phi(3)$.

2. Solve the simultaneous congruence

$$5x \equiv 7 \pmod{8},$$
$$2x \equiv 1 \pmod{3}.$$

3. Find the common solutions to the equations

$$x \equiv j \pmod{3},$$
$$x \equiv k \pmod{5}$$

for the 8 cases $j = 1, 2$ and $k = 1, 2, 3, 4$.

4. In chapter 4 we introduced two functions $d(n)$ and $\sigma(n)$, the number of divisors of n and their sum respectively. Prove that they are multiplicative.

Theorem 7.3 *Euler's totient function is multiplicative.*

PROOF Let m and n be coprime, and let $a_1, \ldots, a_{\phi(m)}$ be the elements of G_m and $b_1, \ldots, b_{\phi(n)}$ be the elements of G_n. We show that every element of G_{mn} arises from one and only one pair (a_j, b_k) and hence that their number $\phi(mn) = \phi(m)\phi(n)$.

First of all given a pair (a_j, b_k) we can create a solution e_{jk} of the simultaneous congruences $x \equiv a_j \pmod{m}$ and $x \equiv b_k \pmod{n}$, by theorem 7.2. The expression for $e_{jk} = a_j c_j n + b_k d_k m$ contains two terms. In the first term a_j, c_j, n are all coprime to m and in the second term b_k, d_k, m are all coprime to n. It follows that e_{jk} is coprime to mn. We can now reduce $e_{jk} \pmod{mn}$ so that it lies in the range 1 to $mn - 1$ and so belongs to G_{mn}. It is also clear that if j or k is altered we must get an altered e_{jk}.

Secondly, given an element e_l belonging to G_{mn} then we can reduce it $\pmod{n}$ to give an element a_j, and since e_l is coprime to mn it follows that a_j is coprime to m and so belongs to G_m. Similarly we can reduce $e_l \pmod{n}$ to give an element b_k which belongs to G_n.

Furthermore if two elements e_s, e_t give rise to the same pair (a_j, b_k), then $e_s \equiv e_t \pmod{m}$ and $e_s \equiv e_t \pmod{n}$, and since m and n are coprime this means $e_s \equiv e_t \pmod{mn}$. In this way we have established a bijection between $G_m \times G_n$ and G_{mn}, thus establishing the theorem. ❑

This theorem enables us to work out $\phi(m)$ for all positive integers m provided $\phi(p^k)$ is known for all primes p and all positive integers k. This is, in fact, quite easy. To determine $\phi(p^k)$ we go back to its definition as the number of positive integers a such that $1 \leq a < p^k$ that are coprime to p^k. But as p is prime these are just the integers that are not multiples p. So we must subtract their number from p^k to get the required amount. The multiples of p are just $1p, 2p, 3p, \ldots, (p^{k-1})p$ and are p^{k-1} in number. Hence

$$\phi(p^k) = p^k - p^{k-1}.$$

For example, $\phi(81) = 3^4 - 3^3 = 81 - 27 = 54$. In general, if we have a composite number such as 1000, we express it in terms of its prime factors and obtain $1000 = 2^3 \times 5^3$ and then, since ϕ is multiplicative

$$\phi(1000) = \phi(2^3)\phi(5^3) = (2^3 - 2^2) \times (5^3 - 5^2) = 4 \times 100 = 400.$$

This enables us to do some wonderful arithmetic.

Example 7.2 If asked to work out the last three digits of 277^{416} we can work (mod 1000) to get

$$277^{416} = 277^{400} \times 277^{16} \equiv 277^{16} \pmod{1000},$$

since 277 is coprime to 1000. Now

$$277^2 \equiv 729 \pmod{1000},$$

so

$$277^4 \equiv 729^2 \equiv 441 \pmod{1000},$$
$$277^8 \equiv 441^2 \equiv 481 \pmod{1000}$$

and

$$277^{16} \equiv 481^2 \equiv 361 \pmod{1000}.$$

Exercise 7e

1. Work out $\phi(37)$, $\phi(464)$ and $\phi(2560)$.

2. Suppose $m = p^a q^b \cdots w^k$ is the decomposition of m into its prime factors, where $p, q, \ldots, w$ are distinct primes and $a, b, \ldots, k$ are positive integers. Prove that

$$\phi(m) = m\left(1 - \frac{1}{p}\right)\left(1 - \frac{1}{q}\right)\cdots\left(1 - \frac{1}{w}\right).$$

Check this formula for $m = 1000$.

3. Show there is a power of 3 that ends with the digits 000 003.

4. For what values of m is $\phi(m) = 10$?

5. For what values of m is $\phi(m) = \frac{1}{2}m$?

6. Evaluate $221^{333} \pmod 9$.

Project 7 In question 4 of project 4 we saw that if $2^n - 1 = p$ is prime, then $2^{n-1}p$ is perfect. The aim of this project is to prove the (harder) converse.

We start with an arbitrary even number written as $2^{n-1}p$ with p odd, $n \geq 2$. This is a perfect number if $\sigma(2^{n-1}p) = 2^n p$.

1. Deduce that $(2^n - 1)\sigma(p) = 2^n p$ and that $2^n - 1 \mid p$.
2. By considering its divisors, show that $p = k(2^n - 1)$ with $k > 1$ leads to a contradiction.
3. Deduce that if $2^{n-1}p$ is perfect, then $2^n - 1 = p$ is prime.
4. Show that an odd perfect number has at least three different prime factors.

Chapter 8

Rational and irrational numbers

8.1 Definitions

The *rational numbers* consist of all the fractions; that is, they are elements of the set Q consisting of all numbers of the form $\frac{m}{n}$, where m and n are integers and $n \neq 0$. When m and n are coprime the rational number is said to be in *reduced form*.

Real numbers which are not rational are called *irrational*. The Greeks were the first to realise that real numbers exist that are not expressible as fractions. Their early geometrical proofs relied upon the fact that a portion of a line segment was expressible as a fractional part of its length, and the discovery that this is not the case caused problems. Nowadays the fact that a right-angled isosceles triangle with shorter sides equal to 1 unit has a hypotenuse equal to $\sqrt{2}$ and that $\sqrt{2}$ cannot be expressed as a fraction is sometimes taken for granted but not proved at secondary school level. From a modern point of view, this fact about $\sqrt{2}$ may seem unremarkable, but for the Greeks it involved a reformulation of some of the basic ideas underlying geometry. It is of interest to see how the problem was overcome: in section 8.5 we consider how Eudoxus achieved this.

Theorem 8.1 *$\sqrt{2}$ is irrational.*

Here are two proofs.

PROOF 1 Suppose $\sqrt{2}$ is rational, then there exist integers m and n, which we may take to be coprime such that $\sqrt{2} = \frac{m}{n}$. Then $m^2 = 2n^2$ and so m^2 and hence m is even. Putting $m = 2M$ we get $2M^2 = n^2$ and so n^2 and hence n is even. This means m and n have the common factor of 2. A contradiction establishes that no such m and n exist. ❑

PROOF 2 If integers m and n exist so that $m^2 = 2n^2$, then let us express each side in terms of its prime factors. Noting that a square has an even number of prime factors and $2n^2$ has an odd number of prime factors, again a contradiction establishes that no such m and n exist. ❑

Not all irrational numbers occur as roots of rational numbers, though any nth root of a rational number (which is not an nth power of a rational number) is irrational. You will have the opportunity to explore this in the next set of exercises. However, irrational numbers may be subdivided. Those that arise as the solutions of polynomial equations whose coefficients are rational numbers are called *algebraic numbers*. Those that do not are called *transcendental numbers*. For example, $7^{\frac{1}{3}}$ is algebraic since it is a solution of the equation $x^3 = 7$, but π is transcendental. To prove that π is irrational is quite difficult, but to prove it is transcendental is very difficult indeed. There has been a lot of research over the last 100 years on transcendental numbers but there is still much that is not known.

Exercise 8a

1. Prove that the sum and product of two rational numbers is rational.

2. Prove that the arithmetic mean of two rational numbers is rational. Deduce that between any two distinct rational numbers, there exist infinitely many rational numbers.

3. (a) Show that if x^n is irrational then so is x.

   (b) More generally, show that if $p(x)$ is irrational (where p is a polynomial with rational coefficients) then so is x.

4. Prove that $\sqrt{3}$ is irrational. Try to prove that $\sqrt{4}$ is irrational with the same method and see where the proof breaks down.

5. Given that the integer N is not a perfect square, prove that $\sqrt{N}$ is irrational.

6. Prove that $\sqrt{2}$, $\sqrt{3}$ and $\sqrt{5}$ cannot be three terms in the same arithmetic sequence.

7. Prove that $\sqrt{2}+\sqrt{3}$ is irrational. Prove further that it is algebraic.

8. Prove that $\sqrt[3]{2}$ is irrational.

9. Prove that if N and n are positive integers, then any solutions of the equation $x^n = N$ are either integer or irrational. [Hint: consider the prime factors of N.]

10. Is it true that

    (a) the sum
    (b) the product

    of two irrational numbers is always irrational?

11. Prove that between any two distinct integers, there always exists an irrational number.

12. Prove that between any two distinct rational numbers, there always exists an irrational number.

13. Prove that the sum and product of a non-zero rational and irrational number are always irrational.

14. Can $x + \dfrac{1}{x}$ be rational with x irrational? How about $x + \dfrac{\sqrt{2}}{x}$?

15. Let N be a positive integer. Show that $\log_{10} N$ is irrational unless N takes a certain form which you should specify.

16. Show that the equation $x^2 = 2^x$ has exactly three real solutions. By mimicking the proof that $\sqrt{2}$ is irrational, show that one of the solutions is irrational.

17. By considering

$$\left(\sqrt{2}^{\sqrt{2}}\right)^{\sqrt{2}},$$

show that there exist positive irrational numbers a and b such that a^b is rational.

8.2 Rational approximations to irrational numbers

A *rational approximation* to an irrational number x is a fraction $\frac{m}{n}$ that is close to x. It is well known that $\frac{22}{7}$ is a rational approximation to π good enough for most practical purposes. A better rational approximation is $\frac{355}{113}$, which agrees with π to 6 decimal places. There are in fact rational numbers arbitrarily close to any irrational number, but mathematicians like to put a measure on facts, so here is a theorem doing just that.

Theorem 8.2 (Dirichlet) *If x is an irrational number, then there are infinitely many pairs of positive integers (a, b) such that $|a - bx| < \frac{1}{b}$.*

Implicit in this theorem is the idea that as b increases, as it is bound to so since there are an infinity of such pairs of integers, we can get an approximation as close to x as we please.

We will prove this theorem for $\sqrt{2}$, though in fact the method we use will work just as well for any irrational number. We will need two ingredients, the notion of the fractional part of a number and the pigeonhole principle.

The *fractional part* of a number x is defined by $\{x\} = x - \lfloor x \rfloor$, where $\lfloor x \rfloor$ is the largest integer smaller than x. For example,

$$\begin{aligned} \{5.4\} &= 5.4 - 4 = 0.4, \\ \{-2.7\} &= -2.7 - (-3) = 0.3, \\ \text{and} \quad \{\sqrt{6}\} &= \sqrt{6} - 2. \end{aligned}$$

Clearly, for all real numbers $0 \leq \{x\} < 1$.

Theorem 8.3 (Pigeonhole principle) *If there are n pigeonholes and $n + 1$ objects to be placed in them, then one of the pigeonholes must have two or more objects in it.*

PROOF Call the assertion $P(n)$. The principle is proved by induction on n.

Clearly if there is 1 pigeonhole and 2 objects then there are 2 objects in that pigeonhole. So $P(1)$ is true.

If $P(k)$ is true, then suppose there are $k+1$ pigeonholes and $k+2$ objects. Take one of the pigeonholes at random. If it has two objects the induction is complete. If it has less than two objects, we are left with k remaining pigeonholes and at least $k+1$ objects, so, from the truth of $P(k)$, one of these remaining pigeonholes has at least two objects and again the induction is complete.

Hence $P(n)$ is true for all positive integers n. ❑

We now look at the proof of theorem 8.2 for the case when the irrational number x is $\sqrt{2}$.

PROOF OF THEOREM 8.2 (WHEN $x = \sqrt{2}$) Let N be a whole number and consider the set of $N+1$ numbers

$$\{\sqrt{2}\},\ \{2\sqrt{2}\},\ \{3\sqrt{2}\}, \ldots,\ \{(N+1)\sqrt{2}\}.$$

These numbers all lie between 0 and 1.

Consider also the number line from 0 to 1 divided into the following N intervals:

$$\begin{gathered} 0 \leq t < \tfrac{1}{N} \\ \tfrac{1}{N} \leq t < \tfrac{2}{N} \\ \tfrac{2}{N} \leq t < \tfrac{3}{N} \\ \vdots \\ \tfrac{N-1}{N} \leq t < 1 \end{gathered}$$

As we have $N+1$ numbers and N intervals, there must be one interval that contains 2 numbers, $\{n\sqrt{2}\}$ and $\{m\sqrt{2}\}$ with $n > m$ say, which lie in the same interval. As each interval has a length of $\frac{1}{N}$,

$$\left|\{n\sqrt{2}\} - \{m\sqrt{2}\}\right| < \frac{1}{N}.$$

But $n\sqrt{2} - m\sqrt{2}$ differs from $\{n\sqrt{2}\} - \{m\sqrt{2}\}$ only by an integer, a say, so setting $b = n - m$, we have $0 < b < N$ and

$$\left|\{n\sqrt{2}\} - \{m\sqrt{2}\}\right| = \left|b\sqrt{2} - a\right|.$$

Hence

$$\left|b\sqrt{2} - a\right| < \frac{1}{N} < \frac{1}{b},$$

as required. ❑

An illustration here might help. Taking $N = 15$, it is easy to check on a calculator that $\{15\sqrt{2}\}$ and $\{3\sqrt{2}\}$ both lie between $\frac{3}{15}$ and $\frac{4}{15}$, and so

$$\left|\{15\sqrt{2}\} - \{3\sqrt{2}\}\right| < \frac{1}{15}.$$

But

$$\{15\sqrt{2}\} - \{3\sqrt{2}\} = 12\sqrt{2} - 17,$$

and so

$$\left|12\sqrt{2} - 17\right| < \frac{1}{15} < \frac{1}{12}.$$

8.3 Iteration

An *iterative procedure* is one in which terms of a sequence may be determined by the values of the terms preceding it. Such procedures can be useful for finding rational approximations to irrational numbers.

Example 8.1 Consider $\sqrt{2}$ as a solution to the equation $x^2 = 2$.

The equation can be rearranged to get

$$(x + 1)(x - 1) = 1$$

and so

$$x - 1 = \frac{1}{x + 1},$$

that is,

$$x = 1 + \frac{1}{x + 1}$$
$$= \frac{x + 2}{x + 1}.$$

From this we can set up the iteration

$$x_{n+1} = \frac{x_n + 2}{x_n + 1},$$

with x_1 a rational number close to $\sqrt{2}$.

Starting with $x_1 = 1$ gives

$$x_2 = \frac{3}{2}, \quad x_3 = \frac{7}{5}, \quad x_4 = \frac{17}{12}, \quad x_5 = \frac{41}{29}.$$

If you keep going, you get

$$x_{13} = \frac{47\,321}{33\,461},$$

which gives $\sqrt{2}$ correct to nine decimal places.

For a satisfactory rational approximation one needs the conjunction of the following conditions:

(i) an iterative scheme for which the formula is fairly straightforward, so that the denominator of the approximating fraction does not get magnified too greatly at each iteration;

(ii) a rapidly convergent scheme;

(iii) the existence of a good first approximation.

Condition (iii) can never be guaranteed, but conditions (i) and (ii) are feasible for the extraction of the pth root of an integer N. The best iteration scheme is a result of the following theorem.

Theorem 8.4 *If $N > 0$ and $\frac{u}{v}$ is a good rational approximation to $N^{\frac{1}{p}}$, where p is a positive integer, then*

$$\frac{U}{V} = \frac{u\{(p-1)u^p + (p+1)v^p N\}}{v\{(p+1)u^p + (p-1)v^p N\}}$$

is a far better approximation, in the sense that if

$$\left(\frac{u}{v}\right)^p = N\left(1 + \frac{\varepsilon}{N}\right) \quad \text{and} \quad \left|\frac{\varepsilon}{N}\right| < 1,$$

then

$$\left(\frac{U}{V}\right)^p = N\left(1 + \mathcal{O}\left(\frac{\varepsilon^3}{N^3}\right)\right).$$

In the statement of the theorem the $\mathcal{O}$ notation means that after N the next term is of order $\frac{\varepsilon^3}{N^3}$. In other words a relative error of $\frac{\varepsilon}{N}$ is converted after just one step of the iteration into a relative error of order $\frac{\varepsilon^3}{N^3}$. The proof of the theorem, which is omitted, is straightforward and depends only on the binomial theorem. The actual value of the cubic term is

$$\frac{(p^2-1)\varepsilon^3}{12p^2N^3}.$$

There are, of course smaller terms after the cubic term.

As an example, if we start with $\frac{u}{v} = \frac{7}{5}$, one iteration to calculate $\sqrt{2}$ gives $\frac{U}{V} = \frac{1393}{985}$, which is correct to better than 4×10^{-7}.

As a second example, if we start with $\frac{u}{v} = \frac{5}{3}$, one iteration to calculate $13^{\frac{1}{5}}$ gives $\frac{U}{V} = \frac{78\,635}{47\,079}$, which is correct to better than 4×10^{-8}.

Exercise 8b

1. In the iteration scheme of example 8.1, set $x_n = \frac{p_n}{q_n}$ where p_n and q_n are coprime integers.
   (a) Express p_{n+1} and q_{n+1} in terms of p_n and q_n.
   (b) Show that $p_n^2 - 2q_n^2 = (-1)^n$.
   (c) Deduce that x_n tends to $\sqrt{2}$ as n tends to infinity.

2. Use a similar method to that in example 8.1 to suggest why the iteration

$$x_{n+1} = \frac{2x_n + 5}{x_n + 2},$$

   with $x_1 = 2$, might be suitable to yield rational approximations to $\sqrt{5}$.

   If p_n and q_n are defined in an analogous way to question 1, prove that $p_n^2 - 5q_n^2 = (-1)^n$ and deduce that x_n tends to $\sqrt{5}$ as n tends to infinity.

3. Find a rational approximation to $5^{\frac{1}{4}}$ correct to 7 decimal places, using theorem 8.4 with starting value $\frac{3}{2}$.

4. Find a rational approximation to $153^{\frac{1}{9}}$ correct to 8 decimal places, using theorem 8.4 with starting value $\frac{7}{4}$.

8.4 Pell equations

From questions 1 and 2 of exercise 8b, it is clear that there is a connection between these iteration schemes and equations of the form

$$u^2 - nv^2 = 1, \tag{8.1}$$

for integer u and v,where n is a positive integer which is not a perfect square. Such equations are incorrectly attributed to Pell. It was Lagrange who first proved that equation (8.1) has infinitely many solutions for each integer n that is not a perfect square, and who showed how to obtain all the solutions by iteration.

The observation that allows us to solve these equations comes from the fact the equation can be written as

$$\left(u + v\sqrt{n}\right)\left(u - v\sqrt{n}\right) = 1.$$

Hence if (u, v) and (a, b) are solutions, then

$$\left(u + v\sqrt{n}\right)\left(u - v\sqrt{n}\right)\left(a + b\sqrt{n}\right)\left(a - b\sqrt{n}\right) = 1$$

which simplifies to

$$(au + bvn)^2 - n(av + bu)^2 = 1$$

after rearranging the brackets and multiplying out. Hence if we know two sets of positive solutions, we can create a new distinct solution. Therefore, if a Pell equation has a solution, it has infinitely many solutions.

Example 8.2 Consider the equation $u^2 - 2v^2 = 1$.

This has solution $(u, v) = (3, 2)$ by observation. Setting $(a, b) = (3, 2)$ then gives us a second solution $(17, 12)$. Setting our second solution as (u, v) and keeping $(a, b) = (3, 2)$ from here onwards gives us the third solution $(99, 70)$. We can simply keep on going.

What we have here is an iteration

$$\begin{aligned} u_{n+1} &= 3u_n + 4v_n \\ v_{n+1} &= 2u_n + 3v_n, \end{aligned}$$

with $u_1 = 3$, $v_1 = 2$, generating infinitely many distinct solutions.

There are two questions that need to be asked here:

(i) Do all Pell equations have at least one solution?

(ii) Can all the solutions of a Pell equation be found in this way?

The answer to both these question is positive—for (ii) we need to start with the solution for which is smallest—and in fact the key to the proofs is Dirichlet's result, theorem 8.2 on page 62. Details of this can be found in [2].

Exercise 8c

1. Find four distinct solutions to the Pell equation $u^2 - 3v^2 = 1$.

2. A triangle has sides of length a, b and c units. The angle opposite the side of length c units is $60°$. Write down an equation in a, b and c, and rearrange it to the form

$$\left(\frac{2c}{2a-b}\right)^2 - 3\left(\frac{b}{2a-b}\right)^2 = 1.$$

   Hence find two such triangles, not congruent to each other, each containing an angle of $60°$ and whose sides are integers.

3. A triangular number is an integer of the form $\frac{1}{2}n(n+1)$ where n is a positive integer. Prove that there are infinitely many triangular numbers which are also perfect squares.

4. Show that the equation

$$1 + 2 + \cdots + m = (m+1) + (m+2) + \cdots + n$$

   has infinitely many positive integer solutions for m and n.

8.5 Eudoxus' definition

We return to the question at the start of the chapter as to how ratios were defined by Eudoxus to avoid the use of rational numbers.

Instead of saying that the ratio of two line segments $AB : CD = m : n$ for some integers m and n, Eudoxus provided the following definition of ratio, whether the quantities involved can be expressed rationally in terms of each other or not.

Eudoxus *Define $a : b = c : d$, where a, b, c, d are any real numbers (which may represent lengths, for example), if and only if for all integers m and n then $ma - nb$ is positive, zero or negative whenever $mc - nd$ is positive, zero or negative respectively.*

This definition contains implicitly the idea that given any ratio $\frac{a}{b}$, then there will be a host of fractions $\frac{n}{m}$ such that $\frac{a}{b} > \frac{n}{m}$. There will also be a host of fractions $\frac{n}{m}$ such that $\frac{a}{b} < \frac{n}{m}$. Possibly, just possibly, there will be some fraction $\frac{n}{m}$ such that $\frac{a}{b} = \frac{n}{m}$. And furthermore, if the same fractions $\frac{n}{m}$ are less than, equal to or greater than $\frac{c}{d}$, then $\frac{a}{b}$ and $\frac{c}{d}$ are the same real number.

This way of defining real numbers is essentially one of the methods employed in modern analysis. It is as if Eudoxus had leaped 2000 years ahead of his time, just as it is now recognised that Archimedes was aware of the limiting processes involved in the rudiments of the integral calculus for calculating areas and volumes. It is even possible to suggest that implicit in Eudoxus' definition is the idea that it is possible to find fractions $\frac{n}{m}$ that get closer and closer to a number that cannot be expressed as a fraction.

Project 8 In example 1.1 on page 5, we applied the Euclidean algorithm to 893 and 705, giving

$$\begin{aligned}893 &= 1 \times 705 + 188,\\705 &= 3 \times 188 + 141,\\188 &= 1 \times 141 + 47,\\141 &= 3 \times 47 + 0.\end{aligned}$$

It is possible to represent this procedure (in reverse order) in terms of rationals as follows:

$$\frac{141}{47} = 3,$$

$$\frac{188}{141} = 1 + \frac{47}{141} = 1 + \frac{1}{3},$$

$$\frac{705}{188} = 3 + \frac{141}{188} = 3 + \cfrac{1}{1 + \cfrac{1}{3}},$$

$$\frac{893}{705} = 1 + \frac{188}{705} = 1 + \cfrac{1}{3 + \cfrac{1}{1 + \cfrac{1}{3}}}.$$

This representation of a fraction is known as a *continued fraction*. It is convenient to write this in condensed form as $[1; 3, 1, 3]$.

1. Use the same method to derive continued fractions for
   (a) $\frac{765}{630}$
   (b) $\frac{430}{259}$.
2. What can be said about the continued fraction representation of a rational in its lowest terms?

It is also possible to derive continued fractions for irrationals. Let α be a real number, greater than 1. Then $\alpha = \lfloor \alpha \rfloor + \{\alpha\}$ (as defined on page 62). Using $\beta = \frac{1}{\{\alpha\}}$, one can now iterate this procedure. It is clear that this process will not terminate, otherwise α would be rational.

3. Use this method to produce a continued fraction expansion for $\sqrt{2}$.
4. Which irrational number is given by the continued fraction

$$[1; 1, 1, 1, \ldots]?$$

5. Find a continued fraction expansion for π and use it to explain why $\frac{355}{113}$ is such a good rational approximation.

Chapter 9

Real numbers and decimal expansions

9.1 Completeness

Loosely, the set of real numbers $\mathbb{R}$ is the totality of all numbers, both rational and irrational and perhaps envisioned as "all the points on the x-axis". Historically, though, the issues involved in defining real numbers were only satisfactorily resolved in the 19th Century after a long and tortuous quest.

It is helpful initially to focus on a specific irrational number such as $\sqrt{2}$. In this case, we can give a geometrical identification of $\sqrt{2}$ as the length of the diagonal of a unit square, but here we consider how $\sqrt{2}$ relates to the set of all rational numbers $\mathbb{Q}$. Certainly, by theorem 8.1 on page 59, $\sqrt{2}$ is not a member of $\mathbb{Q}$, but it may be constructed as the limit of a sequence of rational numbers. One way to do this is to consider the sequence of numbers given by

$$x_1 = 2, \quad x_{n+1} = \frac{1}{2}\left(x_n + \frac{2}{x_n}\right).$$

By construction, each term of the sequence is a rational number and

$$x_n - x_{n+1} = \frac{1}{2}\left(x_n - \frac{2}{x_n}\right) = \frac{x_n^2 - 2}{2x_n},$$

from which we deduce that (x_n) is a decreasing sequence with $x_n > \sqrt{2}$.

The crucial difference between $\mathbb{R}$ and $\mathbb{Q}$ is *completeness*, a property that may be given by several equivalent definitions. Here it is convenient to state it as:

Completeness Property *Any decreasing sequence (x_n) of real numbers which is bounded below (that is, $x_n \geq c$ for some constant c) has a* real *number as its limit.*

(We may equally well state it for increasing sequences of real numbers which are bounded above.) Applying this to our sequence shows that x_n tends to a limit L (written $x_n \to L$ or $\lim_{n\to\infty} x_n = L$) and, from the definition of the sequence, $L = \frac{1}{2}\left(L + \frac{2}{L}\right)$, which forces $L = \sqrt{2}$. Since each term of our sequence is rational, but the limit is irrational, we see that $\mathbb{Q}$ does not have the completeness property.

Intuitively, completeness captures the idea that, starting from $\mathbb{Q}$ and "filling in the gaps" with irrational numbers gives the real numbers with "no gaps", but there are subtleties in making this rigorous. A full treatment starts with $\mathbb{Q}$ then constructs from $\mathbb{Q}$ a system $\mathcal{R}$ which has all the properties—including completeness—that we expect of $\mathbb{R}$ and which we can thus identify with $\mathbb{R}$. For our purposes, it suffices to take for $\mathcal{R}$ (and hence $\mathbb{R}$) the set of all (infinite) decimal expansions. What do we mean by this?

Since

$$1.4^2 = 1.96 < 2 < 12.25 = 1.5^2$$

we have

$$1.4 < \sqrt{2} < 1.5.$$

Similarly,

$$\begin{aligned} 1.41 &< \sqrt{2} < 1.42, \\ 1.414 &< \sqrt{2} < 1.415, \\ 1.4142 &< \sqrt{2} < 1.4143, \\ &\vdots \qquad\quad \vdots \end{aligned}$$

The left-hand decimals represent an increasing sequence with limit $\sqrt{2}$ and we conventionally write $\sqrt{2} = 1.414213562\ldots$ where the devil is in the details of the "$\ldots$". What this means is that (in principle) the calculations above could be continued to give more and more decimal places, but stopping at any stage falls short of $\sqrt{2}$.

Exercise 9a

1. Let $0 < a_1 < b_1$ be rational numbers with $a_1 b_1 = N > 0$. Let

$$a_{n+1} = \frac{2}{\frac{1}{a_n} + \frac{1}{b_n}} \quad \text{and} \quad b_{n+1} = \frac{a_n + b_n}{2}.$$

Show that a_n, b_n are rational numbers satisfying $a_n b_n = N$ and $a_n < a_{n+1} < b_{n+1} < b_n$. Deduce that (a_n) and (b_n) are sequences of rational numbers tending to the limit $\sqrt{N}$.

2. Let $0 < a_1 < b_1$ be real numbers and let

$$a_{n+1} = \sqrt{a_n b_n} \quad \text{and} \quad b_{n+1} = \frac{a_n + b_n}{2}.$$

Show that $0 < a_n < a_{n+1} < b_{n+1} < b_n$ and that

$$0 < b_{n+1} - a_{n+1} < \left(\tfrac{1}{2}\right)^n (b_1 - a_1).$$

Hence show that the sequences (a_n) and (b_n) are convergent with a common limit.

3. Let $a_n = \left(1 + \frac{1}{n}\right)^n$ and $b_n = \left(1 + \frac{1}{n}\right)^{n+1}$.

(a) Show that, if $0 < x < y$, then

$$(n+1)x^n < \frac{y^{n+1} - x^{n+1}}{y - x} < (n+1)y^n. \qquad (9.1)$$

(b) By substituting $x = 1 + \frac{1}{n+1}$ and $y = 1 + \frac{1}{n}$ in (9.1), prove that $a_n < a_{n+1}$.

(c) By substituting $x = 1 - \frac{1}{n}$ and $y = 1 - \frac{1}{n+1}$ in (9.1), prove that $b_n < b_{n-1}$.

(d) Hence show that $a_n < a_{n+1} < b_{n+1} < b_n$ and that the sequences (a_n) and (b_n) tend to a common limit between 2 and 3.

4. (a) Use the fact that $\frac{1}{n(n+1)} = \frac{1}{n} - \frac{1}{n+1}$ to show that if

$$c_n = \frac{1}{1 \times 2} + \frac{1}{2 \times 3} + \cdots + \frac{1}{n(n+1)}$$

then $c_n = 1 - \frac{1}{n+1}$. Deduce that (c_n) is an increasing sequence with limit 1.

(b) Use the fact that

$$\frac{1}{(n+1)^2} < \frac{1}{n(n+1)}$$

and the result of (a) to show that

$$d_n = \frac{1}{1^2} + \frac{1}{2^2} + \cdots + \frac{1}{n^2}$$

is an increasing sequence which is bounded above and hence convergent.

(c) Let

$$e_n = 1 + \frac{1}{1!} + \frac{1}{2!} + \cdots + \frac{1}{n!}.$$

Use the fact that

$$\frac{1}{(n+1)!} \leq \frac{1}{n(n+1)}$$

and the result of (a) to show that (e_n) is an increasing sequence which is bounded above and hence convergent to a limit. Show that this limit is greater than or equal to the limit of the sequence (a_n) analysed in question 3.

9.2 Decimal expansions

We now explore the decimal expansions of real numbers. First we note four features that are worthy of emphasis.

Not every number has a unique decimal expansion. For example,

$$1.000\ldots = 0.999\ldots,$$
$$0.500\ldots = 0.499\ldots,$$
$$0.123\,000\ldots = 0.122\,999\ldots.$$

To "see" the first of these, consider $1 - 0.999\ldots9 = 0.000\ldots1 = (0.1)^n$ for some integer n. Since $(0.1)^n \to 0$ as $n \to \infty$, we see that $0.999\ldots9 \to 1$ as $n \to \infty$, which is what the equality in the first statement "means". The feeling that $0.999\ldots$ is less than 1 arises from the fact that each truncation $0.999\ldots9$ is less than 1, but, as we have seen, the "..." conceals an additional limiting process which is essential to complete the identification of $0.999\ldots$ with 1.

The full decimal expansion of real numbers can be awkward to deal with. Consider, for example, trying to check that $\sqrt{2} \times \sqrt{3} = \sqrt{6}$ using the full decimal expansions of $\sqrt{2}$, $\sqrt{3}$ and $\sqrt{6}$.

Decimal expansions are not the only way of representing real numbers. Obviously, we may use bases other than 10, but we might also use continued fractions as explored in project 8 on page 69.

Depending on any auxiliary properties of the real number involved, there may or may not be efficient methods of finding its decimal expansion. For example, the decimal expansion of π has been calculated to more than 2.6×10^{12} decimal places, but taking this record further is newsworthy.

Some students have difficulty with decimal expansions, and argue that a number such as 147.499 999..., where the 9s go on for ever, is the largest number which is less than, but not equal to, 147.5. It is correct that 147.5 gets rounded up to 148 and anything slightly less gets rounded down. So 147.499 999 999 99 with ten 9s gets rounded down, and so does 147.4 followed by a million 9s. But this does not mean that 147.499 999... gets rounded down.

The resolution of the difficulty lies in the completeness of the real numbers. In this particular case we can define the sequence

$$x_n = 147.4999\ldots9 \quad \text{with } n \text{ 9s.}$$

This is an increasing sequence, bounded above by 147.5, and, by the completeness property, x_n tends to a limit. Once we know that a limit exists we can call it x, and then we have

$$x = 147.499\,999\ldots,$$

so

$$10x = 1\,474.999\,99\ldots$$

and, subtracting,

$$9x = 1327.5$$

so that

$$x = 147.5.$$

In other words the only consistent interpretation is that 147.499 999... is actually equal to 147.5. It is perhaps annoying that there are two apparently different decimal expansions for the same real number, but it is better to have an annoyance than a misconception.

9.3 Recurring decimals

A *terminating decimal* is one like 0.6 or 0.425. It is easily checked that these correspond in fractional form to $\frac{3}{5}$ and $\frac{17}{40}$.

A decimal expansion in which part of the sequence of numbers is repeated for ever is called a *recurring decimal*. A dot notation is used to indicate exactly which sequence recurs. For example:

> $0.\dot{3}$ stands for 0.33333..., where the 3 is repeated indefinitely;
>
> $0.4567\dot{1}2\dot{3}$ stands for 0.4567 123 123 123 123..., where the sequence 123 is repeated indefinitely.

The length of the repeating sequence is called the *period* of the recurring decimal. For instance, $0.\dot{3}$ has period 1 and $0.4567\dot{1}2\dot{3}$ has period 3.

In case there should be any doubt about the calculations which are necessary to find the value of a recurring decimal, let us look more carefully at $0.\dot{1}$. If one stops after n 1s then the value of that number, by definition, is

$$\frac{1}{10} + \frac{1}{100} + \frac{1}{1000} + \cdots + \frac{1}{10^n},$$

and from the work in chapter 4 on geometric progressions we can sum this to get

$$\frac{1}{9}\left(1 - \left(\tfrac{1}{10}\right)^n\right).$$

Clearly as n gets larger what is subtracted from $\frac{1}{9}$ gets smaller and smaller since $\left(\frac{1}{10}\right)^n \to 0$ as $n \to \infty$. So the number 0.111 11... is equal to $\frac{1}{9}$, and similarly 0.999 99... is equal to 1.

We have seen on the previous page the method for converting a recurring decimal into a fraction. There is no doubt that the method always works, though it is a bit messy to write down a general case. Let us just see what happens with $0.546\,75\dot{5}\,74\dot{2}$. First there is the part that does not repeat, which is

$$0.546\,75 = \frac{54\,675}{100\,000}, \\ = \frac{2187}{4000}.$$

We then have to add on the recurring part, which is

$$0.000\,01 \times \frac{5742}{9999} = \frac{29}{5\,050\,000}.$$

So we get a total of

$$\frac{2187}{4000} + \frac{29}{5\,050\,000} = \frac{5\,522\,233}{10\,100\,000}.$$

Exercise 9b

1. Which fractions correspond to
   (a) 0.35,
   (b) 0.862 75?

2. What is the decimal expansion for
   (a) $\frac{19}{20}$,
   (b) $\frac{19}{160}$?

3. Determine in fractional form the following recurring decimals:
   (a) $0.\dot{4}$
   (b) $0.\dot{4}\dot{5}$
   (c) $0.\dot{4}5\dot{9}$
   (d) $0.6\dot{4}5\dot{9}$.
   (e) $0.\dot{5}3846\dot{1}$.
   (f) $0.6\dot{3}$
   (g) $0.5\dot{0}3\dot{7}$
   (h) $0.2375\dot{4}3\dot{2}$.

4. What is a necessary and sufficient condition for a fraction to be represented by a terminating decimal?

9.4 Rational numbers and decimals

A terminating decimal can be written as $\frac{a}{10^k}$ for some k. After appropriate cancelling, this can be written in its lowest terms as $\frac{p}{q}$, where q is a number of the form $2^n \times 5^m$. Conversely, if we start with such a fraction $\frac{p}{q}$, we can convert it to one of the form $\frac{a}{10^k}$ and this can be written as a terminating decimal.

It remains to be shown that all fractions whose denominators, when in their lowest terms, are not of the form $2^n \times 5^m$ convert into recurring decimals. Let us begin by looking at some examples.

Example 9.1 Let us convert $\frac{4}{21}$ into a decimal.
We do this by the usual short division process, as follows:

$$\begin{array}{r|l} & 0.\ 1\ \ 9\ \ 0\ \ 4\ \ 7\ \ 6\ \ 1\ \ 9\ \ldots \\ \hline 21 & 4.\ {}^{4}0\,{}^{19}0\,{}^{1}0\,{}^{10}0\,{}^{16}0\,{}^{13}0\,{}^{4}0\,{}^{19}0\ \ldots \end{array}$$

and it is now clear that the decimal will recur. This is because there has been a repetition of the remainder 4, so from this point on the calculation with replicate the process from the first occurrence of 4. Hence

$$\frac{4}{21} = 0.\dot{1}9047\dot{6}.$$

Example 9.2 The recurrence does not always begin with the first remainder. For example:

$$\begin{array}{r|l} & 0.\ 0\ \ 1\ \ 1\ \ 9\ \ 0\ \ 4\ \ 7\ \ 6\ \ 1\ \ 9\ \ldots \\ \hline 84 & 1.\ {}^{1}0\,{}^{10}0\,{}^{16}0\,{}^{76}0\,{}^{4}0\,{}^{40}0\,{}^{64}0\,{}^{52}0\,{}^{16}0\,{}^{76}0\ \ldots \end{array}$$

gives us the representation

$$\frac{1}{84} = 0.01\,\dot{1}9047\dot{6}.$$

It is easy to see why this always happens. Consider the fraction $\frac{p}{q}$, where, without loss of generality, we can assume that $0 < p < q$ and it is in its lowest terms. The denominator has prime factors other than 2 and 5, so it does not terminate. As we divide, we obtain a sequence of non-zero remainders $r_1, r_2, r_3, \ldots$ and each of these can take $q - 1$ possible values. We will apply the pigeonhole principle (theorem 8.3 on page 62), taking the possible remainders as the pigeonholes and the actual remainders as the objects to be placed; eventually there will be a repeated remainder and so the sequence recurs. If the first occurrence of the repeated remainder is r_k and the second is $r_{k+\ell}$, then the result is a recurring decimal with period ℓ.

We have now established:

Result 9.1 *A rational number can be written either as a terminating decimal or a recurring decimal.*

This in turn means:

Result 9.2 *An irrational number, when written as a decimal, is neither terminating nor recurring.*

This important result allows us to decide whether a number is rational or irrational by examining its decimal expansion.

Exercise 9c

1. Find the recurring decimals for $\dfrac{1}{13}$ and $\dfrac{2}{13}$.

2. Find the remainders that get used in the long divisions to produce these expansions. What has the period of six got to do with the maximum possible period in this case?

3. Work out $0.\dot{3} \times 0.\dot{5}$ as a recurring decimal.

4. Make a list of the recurring decimals for $\dfrac{k}{37}$, $k = 1$ to 36. Comment on your results.

5. Why are the following numbers irrational?

(a) 0.101 001 000 100 001 000 001 00...

(b) 0.123 456 789 101 112 131 415 16...

(c) 0.112 123 123 412 345 123 456...

(d) $\sum_{n=1}^{\infty} 2^{-\frac{1}{2}n(n+1)}$.

9.5 The period of a recurring decimal

We now investigate what determines the period of a recurring decimal. Why, for example, is the period of $\frac{1}{7}$ six and not some other number? The first observation is that when dividing by the integer 7 there can be at most six different remainders; since 7 cannot go exactly into 10, 20, 30, 40, 50, or 60 these six remainders are, of course, 3, 6, 2, 5, 1, 4. A repeat in the working must therefore occur after at most six divisions and so the period is at most six. However, do not think that the recurring expansion for $\frac{1}{p}$, where p is an odd prime, is always $p-1$. For example, $\frac{1}{37} = 0.\dot{0}2\dot{7}$ and has a period of only three.

Another clue about the period is that $\frac{1}{7} = \frac{142\,857}{999\,999}$. In fact, $7 \times 142\,857$ is the first multiple of 7 which consists entirely of 9s. The existence of such a number can be shown by using Fermat's little theorem (page 45). Since $(10, 7) = 1$, we have $10^6 \equiv 1 \pmod 7$. Hence there is an integer k such that $7k = 10^6 - 1$. It might, of course, be possible that $10^2 \equiv 1 \pmod 7$ or $10^3 \equiv 1 \pmod 7$, but it is straightforward to check that this does not, in fact, happen. Hence the period of $\frac{1}{7}$ is 6 rather than 2 or 3.

For any prime p, we have $10^{p-1} \equiv 1 \pmod p$, and the period of $\frac{1}{p}$ is a factor of $p-1$. In the case $p = 37$, we have $10^3 \equiv 1 \pmod{37}$ and $37 \times 27 = 10^3 - 1$, so $\frac{1}{37} = \frac{27}{999} = 0.\dot{0}2\dot{7}$ and therefore $\frac{1}{37}$ has period 3. This confirms what you discovered in question 4 of exercise 9c.

In general, how do we determine which factor of $p-1$ we need, and, in particular, for which primes is the period of the recurring decimal $\frac{1}{p}$ exactly $p-1$? This is related to the (difficult) problem of whether or not 10 is a primitive root modulo p. It turns out that the primes p under 100 for which 10 is a primitive root modulo p are 7, 17, 19, 23, 29, 47, 59, 61 and 97. However, it is possible to construct a table of the primes with a given period by the following simple procedure. We consider, in turn, the prime factorisations of 99, 999, 9999, and so on.

99 $= 3^2 \times 11$, so $99 \equiv 0 \pmod{11}$ and so $10^2 \equiv 1 \pmod{11}$. Hence $\frac{1}{11}$ has period 2.

999 $= 3^3 \times 37$, so $999 \equiv 0 \pmod{37}$ and so $10^3 \equiv 1 \pmod{37}$. Hence $\frac{1}{37}$ has period 3. (Note that the period cannot be 2, since then 37 would have already appeared as a factor of 99.)

9999 $= 3^2 \times 11 \times 101$, so $9999 \equiv 0 \pmod{101}$ and so $10^4 \equiv 1 \pmod{101}$. Hence $\frac{1}{101}$ has period 4. (Note that the period cannot be 2, since then 101 would have already appeared as a factor of 99.)

99 999 $= 3^2 \times 41 \times 271$, so both $\frac{1}{41}$ and $\frac{1}{271}$ have period 5.

999 999 $= 3^3 \times 7 \times 11 \times 13 \times 37$, so both $\frac{1}{7}$ and $\frac{1}{13}$ have period 6.

9 999 999 $= 3^2 \times 239 \times 4649$, so both $\frac{1}{239}$ and $\frac{1}{4649}$ have period 7.

Note that this method has succeeded in finding all the primes p for which $\frac{1}{p}$ has period less than 8, and we also know the periods for the denominators 3, 7, 11 and 13. But that is not a great deal of help in finding the period of the next such denominator, 17. We know that the period is a factor of 16, and that it cannot be 1, 2 or 4, but we still need to check whether it is 8 or 16.

For composite denominators, it is clear that the period of the recurring decimal $\frac{1}{n}$ is a factor of $\phi(n)$, but again it is not obvious which factor. For prime p, if the decimal $\frac{1}{p}$ has period π_p, then the period of the decimal $\frac{1}{p^k}$ is $p^\ell \pi_p$ for some $\ell \leq k-1$; often (but not always) $\ell = k-1$. However, there is one useful result, which we do not prove here.

Result 9.3 *For primes p, q, if the recurring decimals $\frac{1}{p}$ and $\frac{1}{q}$ have periods π_p and π_q, then the period of $\frac{1}{pq}$ is the LCM of π_p and π_q.*

Exercise 9d

1. Continue the process described above to list all the primes for which the recurring decimal has periods 8, 9 and 10.

2. Use result 9.3 to calculate the periods of $\frac{1}{21}$, $\frac{1}{451}$ and $\frac{1}{429}$.

Project 9

1. Write down the recurring decimal for $\frac{1}{7}$, multiply it by 10 and deduce the recurring decimal for $\frac{3}{7}$. Continue this process to show how the decimal expansions for $\frac{1}{7}, \frac{2}{7}, \ldots, \frac{6}{7}$ form a cycle. Show that the sequence of numerators so formed is a geometric progression, reduced modulo 7.
2. Repeat question 1 starting with the recurring decimal for $\frac{1}{17}$.
3. Repeat question 1 starting with the recurring decimal for $\frac{1}{13}$, but this time produce two separate cycles of length 6.
4. What result would you expect starting with $\frac{1}{239}$?
5. An integer is such that when the first digit is transferred to the end the result is three times as large. Find this integer. Is it unique? How does this relate to recurring decimals?
6. An integer is such that when the last digit is transferred to the beginning the result is five times as large. Find this integer. Is it unique?

Chapter 10

Sequences

10.1 Generating functions

Formally, a *sequence* is a function whose domain is the non-negative integers 0, 1, 2, 3, ... In practice, we think of it as a list of numbers a_0, a_1, a_2, ..., denoted (a_n) for short. Up to now, we have always used a_1 for the first term, thus treating the domain as the positive integers 1, 2, 3, ... There is no convention on this and you will find different authors using either method. It will turn out to be convenient in this chapter to begin with a_0 when we introduce generating functions.

In this chapter we are concerned with sequences of integers, although analysis of such sequences often involves irrational numbers and even complex numbers. We suppose there is a *recurrence relation*—some rule or set of rules—that enables us to calculate each a_n from the previous terms $a_0, a_1, a_2, \ldots, a_{n-1}$.

If we form the related sequence $(\bar{a}_n)$ with $\bar{a}_n \equiv a_n \pmod{m}, 0 \leq \bar{a}_n \leq m-1$ we call such a sequence a *sequence modulo m*. If there exist integers N and T such that $\bar{a}_{n+T} = \bar{a}_n$ for all $n \geq N$ then we say that the sequence is a *periodic sequence modulo m* or a *modulo-periodic sequence*. If $N = 0$, so that the sequence starts being periodic from the outset, then we say that the sequence is a *pure periodic sequence*. If T is as small as possible then it is called the *period*. We have already met some periodic sequences in chapter 6 and chapter 7, for example, the powers of $3 \pmod 7$ are 3, 2, 6, 4, 5, 1, 3, 2, 6, 4, 5, 1, 3, 2, ... and form a pure periodic sequence modulo 7 with period 6. Fermat's little theorem (page 45) and theorem 7.1

on page 52, if $(a, m) = 1$, inevitably mean that the sequences of powers $(a^n \pmod{m})$ produce pure periodic sequences modulo m, with period a factor of $\phi(m)$.

By a *generating function* we mean a function f with formula $f(x)$ in closed form which, when expanded, gives the terms of the sequence, so that for sufficiently small values of x we have

$$f(x) \equiv a_0 + a_1 x + a_2 x^2 + a_3 x^3 + \cdots + a_n x^n + \cdots .$$

By determining such functions we can not only obtain the terms of the sequence, but by giving x suitable values we can deduce the sums of some interesting numerical series.

Example 10.1 Consider

$$f(x) \equiv \frac{5}{1-2x} = 5(1 + 2x + 2^2x^2 + \cdots + 2^n x^n + \cdots),$$

so that $a_n = 5 \times 2^n$, which is a geometric sequence first introduced in chapter 4. The series expansion for $f(x)$ is valid for $|x| < \frac{1}{2}$ and putting $x = \frac{1}{3}$ we get

$$5\left(1 + \frac{2}{3} + \frac{4}{9} + \frac{8}{27} + \cdots\right) = 15.$$

Both the geometric and arithmetic sequences can be generated by linear recurrence relations. A $(k+1)$th-order homogeneous linear recurrence relation is one in which a_0, a_1, ..., a_k are given and then $a_{n+k+1} = c_0 a_{n+k} + c_1 a_{n+k-1} + \cdots + c_k a_n$, $n = 0, 1, 2, \ldots$, where c_0, c_1, ..., c_k are constants. In this chapter, unless otherwise stated, all the a_i and c_j are integers. That is to say there are $(k+1)$ starting values and then each term in succession is obtained from the previous $(k+1)$ terms by a linear relationship independent of n. For example, the *Fibonacci sequence* 1, 1, 2, 3, 5, 8, 13, 21, ... is obtained by the second-order *homogeneous* linear recurrence relation $a_0 = 1$, $a_1 = 1$ and $a_{n+2} = a_{n+1} + a_n$, $n = 0, 1, 2, \ldots$, with $c_0 = 1$ and $c_1 = 1$. A linear recurrence relation is made *inhomogeneous* if to the right hand side of the recurrence relation is added a function $g(n)$.

A geometric sequence arises from a first-order homogeneous linear recurrence relation with $a_0 = a$ and $a_{n+1} = ra_n$, $n = 0, 1, 2, \ldots$. However, it is possible to produce the same sequence by the non-linear second-order recurrence relation $a_0 = a$, $a_1 = ar$, $a_{n+2}a_n = a_{n+1}^2$, $n = 0, 1, 2, \ldots$. When solving a problem about a non-linear recurrence relation it is always worthwhile investigating if it is equivalent to a linear one.

Exercise 10a

1. Find the generating function for the geometric series with $a_n = ar^n$, $n = 0, 1, 2, \ldots$, where a and r are constants.

2. Find the generating function for the arithmetic sequence with $a_n = a + nd$, $n = 0, 1, 2, \ldots$, where a and d are constants.

   [You may use the fact that, provided $|x| < 1$, $1 + 2x + 3x^2 + \cdots + (n+1)x^n + \cdots = (1-x)^{-2}$.]

3. Find a second-order homogeneous linear recurrence relation for the arithmetic sequence given by $a_n = 3 + 5n$, $n = 0, 1, 2, \ldots$.

4. Find the generating function for the arithmetic sequence given by $a_n = 3 + 5n$ in the form

$$f(x) \equiv \frac{cx + d}{px^2 + qx + r},$$

   where the constants c, d, p, q, r are to be determined. Can you see the connection between p, q, r and the coefficients of the second-order linear recurrence relation?

10.2 Partial fractions

In what follows knowledge of partial fractions is required. It is assumed that the reader is familiar with adding algebraic fractions. For example,

$$\frac{3}{(x+2)} - \frac{5}{(2x+3)} = \frac{3(2x+3) - 5(x+2)}{(x+2)(2x+3)} = \frac{(x-1)}{(x+2)(2x+3)}.$$

All you need to know is how to work from right to left, rather than from left to right.

Example 10.2 Given

$$\frac{x-1}{(x+2)(2x+3)}$$

you suppose it is equal to

$$\frac{A}{x+2}+\frac{B}{2x+3},$$

where A and B are found by appreciating that

$$A(2x+3)+B(x+2)=x-1 \tag{10.1}$$

for all x. This is achieved if we can arrange

$$\begin{aligned} 2A+B&=1 \\ \text{and} \quad 3A+2B&=-1, \end{aligned}$$

giving $A=3$ and $B=-5$.

Alternatively, we may substitute $x=-2$ in equation (10.1) to see that $-A=-3$ or $A=3$ and substitute $x=-\frac{3}{2}$ to see that $\frac{1}{2}B=-\frac{5}{2}$ or $B=-5$.

If the degree of the numerator is greater than or equal to that of the denominator you must first divide out before following the given procedure for what remains.

Since any real polynomial can be factorised into linear and quadratic factors over the real numbers, it follows that we have to cope with cases in which the denominator contains quadratic factors. Also we need to know how to handle repeated linear factors. The following example should make this clear.

Example 10.3 If we add the algebraic fractions

$$\frac{5}{x-3}+\frac{2}{(x-3)^2}-\frac{2x+1}{x^2+x+1}$$

we get

$$\frac{3x^3 + 3x^2 - 20x - 22}{(x-3)^2(x^2+x+1)}.$$

The question then is how to work backwards. Well, for the repeated factor $(x-3)^2$ you put

$$\frac{A}{x-3} + \frac{B}{(x-3)^2}$$

or you could put

$$\frac{Ex+F}{(x-3)^2},$$

(but it is more useful in applications to adopt the first expression). For the quadratic factor x^2+x+1 you put

$$\frac{Cx+D}{(x^2+x+1)}.$$

So you try to find A, B, C, D so that

$$3x^3 + 3x^2 - 20x - 22$$
$$= A(x-3)(x^2+x+1) + B(x^2+x+1) + (Cx+D)(x-3)^2$$

for all x. Putting $x = 3$ gives $13B = 26$ so $B = 2$. Equating the coefficients of x^3 you get $A + C = 3$. Equating the constant terms you get $-3A + B + 9D = -22$. Putting $x = 2$ you get $-7A + 7B + 2C + D = -26$. These equations lead to $A = 5$, $B = 2$, $C = -2$, $D = -1$. (You could also have found relevant equations by equating coefficients of x^2, x or substituting other values of x.)

Exercise 10b

1. Put into partial fractions

(a) $\dfrac{12x-13}{(2x-3)(3x-2)}$

(b) $\dfrac{2x^2}{x^2-4}$

(c) $\dfrac{x^2-2x-1}{(x+1)^2(2x^2+2x+1)}$

(d) $\dfrac{x}{x^3-12x+16}$.

10.3 Homogeneous linear recurrence relations

Theorem 10.1 *Let the sequence (a_n) be defined by $a_0 = a$, $a_1 = b$, $a_{n+2} = ca_{n+1} + da_n$, $n = 0, 1, 2, \ldots$, where a, b, c, d are constants, then the generating function for the sequence (a_n) is given by*

$$f(x) \equiv \frac{a+(b-ca)x}{1-cx-dx^2}.$$

PROOF Nothing more is required than to verify

$$(1-cx-dx^2)(a+bx+a_2x^2+a_3x^3+\cdots) = a+(b-ca)x.$$

That the constant terms and the coefficients of x are equal follows by inspection, and that all other coefficients vanish follows from the recurrence relation. Of course the series expansion is only valid for values of x satisfying $|cx+dx^2| < 1$, but that only matters if we want to make a deduction by giving x a certain value. ❑

We give some examples of the use of theorem 10.1.

Example 10.4 Find the nth term of the sequence defined by $a_0 = 1$, $a_1 = 11$, $a_{n+2} = 5a_{n+1} - 6a_n$, $n = 0, 1, 2, \ldots$.

Here $a = 1$, $b = 11$, $c = 5$, $d = -6$, so the generating function

$$f(x) \equiv \frac{1+6x}{1-5x+6x^2} = \frac{1+6x}{(1-2x)(1-3x)} = \frac{9}{1-3x} - \frac{8}{1-2x},$$

in partial fraction form.

It follows that

$$f(x) \equiv 9(1 + 3x + \cdots + 3^n x^n + \cdots) - 8(1 + 2x + \cdots + 2^n x^n + \cdots)$$

and hence that $a_n = 9 \times 3^n - 8 \times 2^n = 3^{n+2} - 2^{n+3}$.

Example 10.5 Find the nth term of the Fibonacci sequence defined by $a_0 = 1$, $a_1 = 1$, and $a_{n+2} = a_{n+1} + a_n$, $n = 0, 1, 2, \ldots$.
Here $a = 1, b = 1, c = 1, d = 1$, so the generating function is

$$f(x) \equiv \frac{1}{1 - x - x^2}.$$

Now let $\alpha = \frac{1}{2}(1 + \sqrt{5})$ and $\beta = \frac{1}{2}(1 - \sqrt{5})$, so that

$$f(x) \equiv \frac{1}{(1 - \alpha x)(1 - \beta x)},$$

since $\alpha + \beta = 1$ and $\alpha\beta = -1$. In partial fractions this becomes

$$f(x) \equiv \frac{1}{\sqrt{5}} \left(\frac{\alpha}{1 - \alpha x} - \frac{\beta}{1 - \beta x} \right)$$

from which we get Binet's famous formula

$$a_n = \frac{1}{\sqrt{5}} \left(\alpha^{n+1} - \beta^{n+1} \right).$$

Of course it does not look at first sight that this expression for a_n is an integer, but this may be checked to be true. Since $|\beta| < 1$, it follows that

$$a_n \approx \frac{1}{\sqrt{5}} \alpha^{n+1},$$

the approximation being increasingly good for large n. For instance $a_{10} = 89$ and

$$\frac{1}{\sqrt{5}} \alpha^{11} = 88.997\,75$$

to 5 decimal places. Its exact value is

$$\frac{199\sqrt{5}}{10} + \frac{89}{2}$$

and as an approximation to 89 it provides $\frac{199}{89}$ as a rational approximation to $\sqrt{5}$, which is correct to 3 decimal places. Another interesting fact is that the ratio of consecutive terms

$$\frac{a_{n+1}}{a_n} \to \alpha \text{ as } n \to \infty.$$

The number $\alpha = \frac{1}{2}(1 + \sqrt{5})$ is the *golden ratio*, a number that occurs frequently in geometrical and numerical problems. And architecturally, if the length to the height of a room is in the ratio $\alpha : 1$ it is supposed to be particularly pleasing to the eye.

Example 10.6 Find the nth term of the sequence defined by $a_0 = 0$, $a_1 = 3$ and $a_{n+2} = 8a_{n+1} - 25a_n$, $n = 0, 1, 2, \ldots$.

This is an example of an oscillating sequence with increasing amplitude, and the method of solution by means of a generating function involves the use of complex numbers. So, if you have not used complex numbers before, you can omit the working below, and instead prove by induction that the answer is $a_n = 5^n \sin n\phi$, where $\phi = \arctan \frac{3}{4}$.

In this example we have $a = 0, b = 3, c = 8, d = -25$, so the generating function is

$$\begin{aligned} f(x) &\equiv \frac{3x}{1 - 8x + 25x^2} \\ &= \frac{3x}{(1 - (4+3i)x)(1 - (4-3i)x)} \\ &= \frac{i}{2}\left(1 - 5e^{-i\phi}x\right)^{-1} - \frac{i}{2}\left(1 - 5e^{i\phi}x\right)^{-1}. \end{aligned}$$

The coefficient of x^n in the expansion of $f(x)$ is

$$\tfrac{1}{2}i\,5^n e^{-in\phi} - \tfrac{1}{2}i\,5^n e^{in\phi} = 5^n \sin n\phi.$$

Exercise 10c

1. The sequence (a_n) is defined by $a_0 = 0, a_1 = 2, a_{n+2} = 4(a_{n+1} - a_n)$. For which values of n is a_n a power of 2?

2. Find a second-order homogeneous linear recurrence relation for the sequence whose nth term is

$$\frac{1}{\sqrt{3}}\left(\alpha^{n+1} - \beta^{n+1}\right),$$

where $\alpha = 1 + \sqrt{3}$ and $\beta = 1 - \sqrt{3}$.

3. Find the generating function for the sequence whose nth term is n^2, and hence find a third-order homogeneous linear recurrence relation for this sequence. Hence find the sum of the infinite series whose nth term is

$$\frac{n^2}{2^n}.$$

4. The sequence (a_n) is defined by $a_0 = 1, a_1 = 3, a_{n+2} = 2a_{n+1} - 2a_n$, $n = 0, 1, 2, \ldots$. Find a closed form expression for a_n.

5. Formulate and prove a theorem analogous to theorem 10.1 for homogeneous linear recurrence relations of the third order.

10.4 Modulo-periodic sequences

It turns out that a sequence of integers derived by a set of rules is very often a periodic sequence modulo m. We first give a number of examples to illustrate the idea.

Example 10.7

(a) The sequence $\left(n^2 \pmod{10}\right)$ is

$$0, 1, 4, 9, 6, 5, 6, 9, 4, 1, 0, 1, \ldots$$

with a period of 10.

(b) The sequence $(n^2 \pmod 4)$ is

$$0, 1, 0, 1, \ldots$$

with a period of 2.

(c) The Fibonacci sequence

$$1, 1, 2, 3, 5, 8, 13, 21, 34, 55, 89, 144, \ldots$$

$\pmod 7$ becomes

$$1, 1, 2, 3, 5, 1, 6, 0, 6, 6, 5, 4, 2, 6, 1, 0, 1, 1, \ldots$$

with a period of 16.

(d) The sequence $(3^n \pmod{11})$ is

$$1, 3, 9, 5, 4, 1, 3, \ldots$$

with a period of 5.

You will recognise that example 10.7(d) is a consequence of Fermat's little theorem. For this gives $3^{10} \equiv 3^0 \pmod{11}$ and so, as in theorem 6.3, a period must exist and must be a factor of 10. It is useful to have some general theorems to cover other integer sequences, so that one is not confronted with having to create *ad hoc* proofs of their periodicity. Of course the proofs of the periodicity in example 10.7(a) and (b) are very easy, and the periodicity in example 10.7(c) is not too difficult, once you realise that the initial conditions $\pmod 7$ recur as the seventeenth and eighteenth terms.

As in section 10.1, we use the notation $(\bar{a}_n) = (a_n \pmod m)$. First we prove a very general theorem.

Theorem 10.2 *Suppose that (a_n) is a sequence of integers in which*

$$a_{n+r} = F(a_{n+r-1}, a_{n+r-2}, \ldots, a_n),$$

where F is a polynomial in r variables with integer coefficients, then $(\bar{a}_n)$ is a periodic sequence.

PROOF The reason F is taken to be a polynomial with integer coefficients is to ensure that all a_n in the sequence are integers. Consider the ordered r-tuples

$$(\bar{a}_0, \bar{a}_1, \ldots, \bar{a}_{r-1}),\ (\bar{a}_1, \bar{a}_2, \ldots, \bar{a}_r),\ \ldots,\ (\bar{a}_k, \bar{a}_{k+1}, \ldots, \bar{a}_{k+r-1}),\ \ldots$$

where two r-tuples are equal if and only if all r entries are equal. Since each entry can take on only m values the number of distinct r-tuples is m^r. It follows that eventually there must be a repeat. Since the function F depends only on the values $\pmod{m}$ of the elements of the r-tuple, once the repeat has occurred all succeeding values recur with the same period. ❑

If $T(m)$ is the least integer such that $\bar{a}_{n+T} = \bar{a}_n$ for all $n \geq N$ then $T(m)$ is called the *period* modulo m.

Theorem 10.3 *If $S(m)$ is any integer such that $\bar{a}_{n+S} = \bar{a}_n$ for all $n \geq N$ then $T(m) \mid S(m)$.*

PROOF Suppose not, then by the Euclidean algorithm $S = Tq + r$, where $0 < r < T$ and $\bar{a}_n = \bar{a}_{n+S} = \bar{a}_{n+Tq+r} = \bar{a}_{n+r}$ for all $n \geq N$, contradicting the hypothesis that T is the least integer with this property. ❑

It is clear that for a sequence generated as above it will not only be a periodic sequence modulo m, but also a periodic sequence modulo m^* for any other integer $m^* > 1$. In general the periods $T(m)$ and $T(m^*)$ are unrelated. However it is clear that if $m^* \mid m$, then $T(m^*) \mid T(m)$. This is because if $a_{n+T(m)} \equiv a_n \pmod{m}$ for all $n \geq N$, then $a_{n+T(m)} \equiv a_n \pmod{m^*}$ for all $n \geq N$ and so by theorem 10.3 $T(m^*) \mid T(m)$.

Theorem 10.4 *Let M denote $[m, m^*]$, the lowest common multiple of m and m^*. Then $T(M) = [T(m), T(m^*)]$*

PROOF Since $m \mid M$ and $m^* \mid M$ it follows from the text prior to the theorem that $T(m) \mid T(M)$ and $T(m^*) \mid T(M)$ and hence $[T(m), T(m^*)] \mid T(M)$. Furthermore, we have

$$a_{n+[T(m),T(m^*)]} \equiv a_n \text{ both } \pmod{m} \text{ and } \pmod{m}^*,$$

for all $n \geq N$, so that

$$a_{n+[T(m),T(m^*)]} \equiv a_n \pmod{[m, m^*]}$$

for all $n \geq N$, and hence by theorem 10.3 we have

$$T(M) \mid [T(m), T(m^*)].$$ ❑

Exercise 10d

1. Show how the periodicity of the four sequences in example 10.7 may be deduced from theorem 10.2.

2. Prove that if (c_n) and (d_n) are two periodic modulo m sequences with periods T_c and T_d respectively then $(c_n + d_n)$, $(c_n - d_n)$ and $(c_n d_n)$ are periodic modulo m with period a factor of $[T_c, T_d]$.

3. Prove that the sequence $(a_n \pmod{m})$, where $a_n = n^3$ is a pure periodic sequence with period a factor of m.

4. Prove that the sequence $(a_n \pmod{6})$, where $a_n = n^3 + 8n$ is periodic, and find its period.

5. In the Fibonacci sequence defined in example 10.5, are there any terms whose last digit is 0?

6. In the sequence defined by $a_0 = 1, a_1 = 2, a_{n+2} = 2a_{n+1} - a_n, n \geq 0$, find the period of $a_n \pmod{7}$.

Theorem 10.5 *Suppose that (a_n) is a sequence defined by the homogeneous linear recurrence relation $a_{n+2} = k_1 a_{n+1} + k_2 a_n$, $n \geq 0$, where a_0, a_1, k_1, k_2 are integers, then $(a_n \pmod{m})$ is a pure periodic sequence $\pmod{m}$ provided $(k_2, m) = 1$. In particular it is pure periodic if $k_2 = \pm 1$.*

Note that the theorem generalises to homogeneous linear recurrence relations of higher order than 2.

PROOF From theorem 10.2 we know that $(a_n \pmod m)$ is a periodic sequence modulo m. That is there exist natural numbers N and T such that $a_{n+T} \equiv a_n \pmod m$ for all $n \geq N$. From the recurrence relation we have

$$\begin{aligned} k_2 a_{N+T-1} &= a_{N+T+1} - k_1 a_{N+T} \\ &\equiv a_{N+1} - k_1 a_N \pmod m \\ &\equiv k_2 a_{N-1} \pmod m, \end{aligned}$$

and since $(k_2, m) = 1$ it follows that $a_{N+T-1} \equiv a_{N-1} \pmod m$. Continuing this process backwards a total of N times we see that $a_T = a_0 \pmod m$ so that $(a_n \pmod m)$ is pure periodic. ❑

An immediate corollary is that $(a_n \pmod p)$ is pure periodic if p is prime and provided k_2 is not a multiple of p.

Theorem 10.6 *If $(a, m) = 1$, then $(a^n \pmod m)$ is pure periodic with period a factor of $\phi(m)$, where ϕ is Euler's totient function.*

PROOF Since $a_{n+2} = a^2 a_n$ and $(a, m) = 1$ so that $(a^2, m) = 1$, the sequence is pure periodic from theorem 10.5 with $k_1 = 0$, $k_2 = a^2$. Since $a^{\phi(m)} \equiv a^0$, by theorem 10.3 the period is a factor of $\phi(m)$. ❑

Exercise 10e

1. Find the period of $(a^n \pmod{10})$ for all positive integers a.

2. Prove that $(n^n \pmod{10})$ is a pure periodic sequence of period 20.

3. Find all integers n such that $11 \mid (2^n + 1)$.

4. Given $a_0 = 0$, $a_1 = 1$, $a_{n+2} = 3a_{n+1} - a_n$, $n \geq 0$, show that a_{2n+1} is never divisible by 2001 for any positive integer n.

5. Formulate and prove a version of theorem 10.5 for third-order homogeneous recurrence relations.

Project 10

1. For the Fibonacci sequence find the period (mod m) for all integers $m = 2$ to 10.
2. Let S_n be the sum of the first n terms of the Fibonacci sequence. Investigate the period of the sequence $\left(S_n \pmod{m}\right)$ for $m = 2$ to 10.
3. Repeat questions 1 and 2 for the sequence of square numbers.

Part II

Solving problems

Chapter 11

Numbers and digits

11.1 Divisibility rules

Some problems set in competitions concern the representation of numbers in base 10, and require little more than a knowledge of the divisibility rules, as in section 3.4 on page 25.

Example 11.1 Given that

$$34! = 295\,232\,799\,cd9\,604\,140\,847\,618\,609\,643\,5ab\,000\,000$$

determine the digits a, b, c and d. *[BMO1 Dec 2002]*

It is possible, if you have the patience and accuracy, to calculate 34! and obtain a solution this way. However, that was not the intention of the setters. A good first step is to produce the prime factorisation of 34! at least as far as the prime 11, since we can then appeal to the well-known divisibility rules for 2, 3, 5, 9 and 11.

The way to do this is to form a sort of tally for each prime; the factor 7, for example, appears once each for 7, 14, 21 and 28, and hence four times altogether in the factorisation of 34!. Hence $34! = K \times 11^3 \times 7^4 \times 5^7 \times 3^{15} \times 2^{32}$, where K is a product of primes greater than 11.

From the factor 5^7 we see that 34! has exactly seven 0s at the end, so $b = 0$ and $a > 0$. Leaving aside these seven digits, what remains is divisible by 8, and, since 1000 is divisible by 8, the same must be true of '35a'; it follows that $a = 2$.

Next we have a divisor of 9, so the digit sum is also divisible by 9. This tells us that $c + d$ is either 3 or 12. Now we apply the divisibility test for 11, which concerns the sums of even and odd digits; this gives us the options $d - c = 3$ or $c - d = 8$. We can now deduce that $c = 0$ and $d = 3$, so $(a, b, c, d) = (2, 0, 0, 3)$.

Exercise 11a

1. The five-digit number '$a679b$' is divisible by 36. Find all possible such five-digit numbers. *[Cayley 2005]*

2. (a) A positive integer N is written using only the digits 2 and 3, with each appearing at least once. If N is divisible by 2 and by 3, find the smallest possible value of N.

   (b) A positive integer M is written using only the digits 8 and 9, with each appearing at least once. If M is divisible by 8 and by 9, find the smallest possible value of M.

   [Hamilton 2004]

3. Find the smallest positive integer which consists only of 0s and 1s when written in base 10 and which is divisible by 12. *[Hamilton 2006]*

4. Find the smallest positive multiple of 35 whose digits are all the same as each other. *[Maclaurin 2006]*

11.2 Place value representation

Other problems begin with nothing more complex than the recognition that a number which is written as 1356, say, in base 10 is actually $1 \times 1000 + 3 \times 100 + 5 \times 10 + 6$. The solution to the problem often begins with some condition which allows us to deduce an equation and then we have to find all possible values of the digits which will satisfy this equation.

Example 11.2 All the digits of a certain positive three-digit number are non-zero. When the digits are taken in reverse order a different number is formed. The difference between the two numbers is divisible by eight. Given that the original number is a perfect square, find its possible values. *[Maclaurin 2009]*

Since the number is three-digit, we can write it as $100a + 10b + c$, and we are told that none of a, b, c are zero, so they are each between 1 and 9. Moreover, reversing the order of the digits produces a different number—or, in other words, it is not a palindrome. This tells us that $a \neq c$. The reverse number is $100c + 10b + a$, and the difference between them is $99(a - c)$. This can be positive or negative, but it cannot be zero, and we are told that it is divisible by 8. However, 8 and 99 are coprime, so it follows that $8 \mid (a - c)$, and since $a - c \neq 0$, it can only take two values, 8 and -8. This now means that there are only two possibilities for the pair (a, c); it is either $(9, 1)$ or $(1, 9)$. Finally, we are told that the number is a perfect square, so we consider all numbers of the form '$1b9$' or '$9b1$' testing which of them fulfil that condition. There are exactly two such numbers, 169 and 961.

This is a fairly neat and direct solution, but it is not the only one. It is in fact a criticism of this problem that it can be approached, in a much less elegant way, by making a list of all possible three-digit numbers and searching through the list to find those which satisfy all of the conditions. The drawback of any method based on 'exhaustive search' is that it is up to you to convince the marker that you really have considered all the possibilities. It is certainly not good enough just to state that you listed all the three-digit numbers on a sheet of rough paper, went through them one by one and emerged with the answers 169 and 961. What you have to demonstrate is that you have considered all the possibilities, eliminated the wrong answers carefully and checked that all those which remain are satisfactory.

In this case, you need not consider all 900 three-digit numbers. First of all, you can leave out any with a digit of zero and then all the palindromes. Being a little more sophisticated, you can omit all those whose first and last digits are of opposite parity (since then there is no chance of the difference between the number and the reverse dividing by 8). In fact, the most sensible strategy is to list all the three-digit perfect squares; there are only 22 of them, and it is easy to check them all. Even so, it is worth explaining how you know that there are exactly 22 and that you are not missing any. Note that even the algebraic approach given above reduces to a search at the final stage.

On the whole, good Olympiad problems discourage candidates from using crude search methods. This is done both by making the 'number pool' so big that the approach is unfeasible, and avoiding straightforward filters such as the condition of being a perfect square. In what follows, we concentrate on more sophisticated methods of solution.

Example 11.3 Given a three-digit number n, we obtain a new number $f(n)$ which is equal to the sum of the three digits of n, their three products in pairs and the product of all three digits. Find all such numbers n such that $f(n) = n$. *[BMO1 Jan 1994, adapted]*

It is clear that exhaustive search is not an efficient technique for this problem, so you are forced into adopting an algebraic approach. Letting the base 10 representation of n be 'abc', we are led to the equation

$$100a + 10b + c = a + b + c + ab + bc + ca + abc. \qquad (11.1)$$

How can the two sides of this equation be equal? What strikes you immediately is the presence of the $100a$ term on the left, which is going to mean that the digits b and c are going to have to be fairly big in order to make equality possible. If, for example, you experiment by taking $a = 1$, you obtain the equation $99 + 10b + c = 2(b + c + bc)$. If $b = c = 8$, then the left-hand side is 187 and the right-hand side is only 160, which is a sizeable shortfall.

After a while, you begin to suspect that the only solution to this equation is $b = c = 9$, which gives a maximum value of 99 for $b + c + bc$. In order to prove this, it is worth trying to rearrange equation (11.1) so as to focus on this term. On the right-hand side of equation (11.1) we have $a(b + c + bc)$. Given that factorised forms are always useful in problem-solving, we are eventually led to the rearrangement

$$b(9 - c) = a(b + c + bc - 99).$$

Now it is clear that the maximum value of the right-hand side is 0, since $a > 0$ and $b + c + bc \leq 99$. On the other hand, the left-hand side cannot be negative, so the only possibility of equality is when both sides are zero. We have achieved our aim of showing that $b = c = 9$, and clearly a can take any value. So n is any number of the form 'a99'.

To summarise, the sort of techniques which are useful in solving this type of problem include:

- representation of numerals in place-value notation in algebraic form;
- algebraic rearrangement of an expression into factors;
- magnitude considerations, given that digits are at most 9;
- parity checks;
- properties of primes;
- divisibility properties.

Exercise 11b

1. An *unfortunate* number is a positive integer which is equal to 13 times the sum of its digits. Find all unfortunate numbers.
   [Hamilton 2005]

2. A two-digit number is n times the sum of its digits, where n is a positive integer. A new number is formed by reversing the digits of the original number. The new number is k times the sum of its digits. Find the value of k. *[Maclaurin 2003, adapted]*

3. From a three-digit number (with no repeated digit and no zero digits) we can form six two-digit numbers by choosing all possible ordered pairs of digits. For example, the number 257 produces the six numbers 25, 52, 57, 75, 27 and 72. Find all such three-digit numbers for which the sum of the six two-digit numbers is equal to the original three-digit number. *[Maclaurin 2005]*

4. Find, showing your method, a six-digit integer n with the following properties:

   (a) the number formed by the last three digits of n is exactly one greater than the number formed by the first three digits of n (so n might be 123 124);

   (b) n is a perfect square.

   [BMO1 Jan 1993]

5. Find all pairs m, n of positive integers satisfying the following conditions:

(a) two of the digits of m are the same as the corresponding digits of n, whilst the other digits of m are both 1 less than the corresponding digits of n;

(b) both m and n are four-digit squares.

[BMO1 Jan 1996]

11.3 Harder problems

More sophisticated problems sometimes work with other bases, notably binary, and require the use of congruence arithmetic or more ingenious methods.

Example 11.4 When written in base 2, a multiple of 17 contains exactly three digits 1. Prove that it contains at least six digits 0, and that if it contains exactly seven digits 0, then it is even. *[BMO1 Mar 1982]*

Let the number be N and let its binary representation be $2^a + 2^b + 2^c$, with $a > b > c \geq 0$; note that we are using the knowledge that there are exactly three digits which are 1. All that we know in addition to this is that fact that N has a factor of 17. Since no power of 2 has a factor of 17, we can conclude that $17 \mid (2^{a-c} + 2^{b-c} + 1)$.

At this point, we should be wondering how powers of 2 behave when divided by 17. Working modulo 17, we find that the residues of 2^n for $n \geq 0$ form a cycle 1, 2, 4, 8, -1, -2, -4, -8, so that $2^{n+8} \equiv 2^n \pmod{17}$. Hence the three residues corresponding to the three terms of $2^{a-c} + 2^{b-c} + 1$ sum to zero, and they are therefore, in order, either 8, 8 and 1, or -2, 1 and 1, or 1, -2 and 1.

We now consider each case individually. In the first case, we must have $a - c \equiv 3 \pmod 8$ and $b - c \equiv 3 \pmod 8$, with $a > b$, so the smallest such N has binary representation 100 000 001 001 (corresponding to $a = 11$, $b = 3$, $c = 0$). This twelve-digit number has nine zeros, and larger values of N will have more. In the second case, we have $a - c \equiv 5$

$\pmod 8$ and $b - c \equiv 0 \pmod 8$, with $a > b > c$, and now the smallest example is 10 000 100 000 001 (corresponding to $a = 13$, $b = 8$, $c = 0$) and has eleven zeros. In the third case, we have $a - c \equiv 0 \pmod 8$ and $b - c \equiv 5 \pmod 8$, with $a > b > c$, and now the smallest example is 100 100 001 (corresponding to $a = 8$, $b = 5$, $c = 0$) and has six zeros.

Finally, if we want a number with exactly seven zeros, it can only be 1 001 000 010, and this is even.

Exercise 11c

1. Find all positive integers whose squares end in three 4s, and show that no perfect square ends in four 4s. *[BMO1 Jan 1995, adapted]*

2. Prove that there is no proper fraction $\frac{m}{n}$ with denominator $n \leq 100$ whose decimal expansion contains the block of consecutive digits 167 in that order. *[BMO1 Mar 1978]*

3. Find all two-digit positive integers N for which the sum of the digits of $10^N - N$ is divisible by 170. *[BMO1 Jan 2001]*

4. Consider all numbers of the form $3n^2 + n + 1$, where n is a positive integer. Call the sum of the digits, in base 10, the *digisum*.

   (a) How small can the digisum of such a number be?

   (b) Can such a number have a digisum equal to 1999?

   [BMO2 Feb 1999]

Chapter 12

Prime numbers and divisibility

12.1 Linear combinations and factorisation

The most straightforward problems involve the factorisation of positive integers and the properties of the highest common factor and lowest common multiple.

Example 12.1 Prove that, if a, b, c, d, e are positive integers, any common factor of $ae + b$ and $ce + d$ is also a factor of $ad - bc$.

[BMO1 Mar 1969]

When this problem was set, there was little or no training available to those who sat the Olympiads and very few, if any, accessible books which focused on basic number theory. The internet, of course, was not even dreamt about! Hence it was possible to set a question as easy as this. In fact, all you need to know is theorem 1.1 on page 4 about linear combinations of expressions.

Our aim, then, is to try to write the expression $ad - bc$ in terms of the other two, and soon discover that

$$ad - bc = a(ce + d) - c(ae + b).$$

If, therefore, $n \mid (ce + d)$ and $n \mid (ae + b)$, it immediately follows that $n \mid (ad - bc)$.

It is also useful to know the most important factorisations of algebraic expressions.

Example 12.2 Show that, for every positive integer n, the number $121^n - 25^n + 1900^n - (-4)^n$ is divisible by 2000. *[BMO1 Jan 2000]*

Here is it tempting to start by doing a lot of arithmetic, but actually it is much more useful to look at the sort of expressions which occur in $121^n - 25^n + 1900^n - (-4)^n$, which we will call N. When we do so, we should be reminded of the factorisation

$$x^n - y^n \equiv (x - y)\left(x^{n-1} + x^{n-2}y + \cdots + xy^{n-2} + y^{n-1}\right).$$

The significance of this is that $x - y$ is always a factor of $x^n - y^n$. There are ways to choose the values of x and y which will turn out to be useful.

For example, taking $x = 121$ and $y = 25$, we see that $96 \mid (121^n - 25^n)$, and taking $x = 1900$ and $y = -4$, we see that $1904 \mid (1900^n - (-4)^n)$. Hence the highest common factor of 96 and 1904 is a factor of N, and a little calculation shows that this is 16.

Now we regroup the expressions to gain more information. Take $x = 121$ and $y = -4$ to get $125 \mid (121^n - (-4)^n)$, and $x = 1900$ and $y = 25$ to obtain $1875 \mid (1900^n - 25^n)$. Hence the highest common factor of 125 and 1875, which is 125, is a factor of N. We now have two factors of N, namely 16 and 125, and what is important is that these are co-prime. Hence their product (or, to put it another way, lowest common multiple) also divides into N, and this is 2000.

Exercise 12a

1. Find four prime numbers less than 100 which are factors of $3^{32} - 2^{32}$. *[BMO1 Dec 2006]*

2. Let n be an integer greater than 6. Prove that if $n-1$ and $n+1$ are both prime, then $n^2(n^2+16)$ is divisible by 720.
   Is the converse true? *[BMO1 Nov 2005]*

3. Find all non-negative integers n such that $5^n - 4^n$ has a factor of 61. *[BMO1 Mar 1967]*

4. Find all positive integers n such that $n+2008$ is a factor of n^2+2008 and $n+2009$ is a factor of n^2+2009. *[BMO1 Dec 2008]*

5. The Fibonacci sequence (F_n) is defined as follows:

$$F_1 = 1, \quad F_2 = 1, \quad F_{k+2} = F_k + F_{k+1} \ (k > 0).$$

   Prove that, for all positive integers n, there are unique integers a, b, m such that $0 < a, b < m$ and $m \mid (F_n - anb^n)$. *[BMO1 Jan 1983]*

12.2 Coprime numbers and the Euclidean algorithm

It is always worthwhile trying to factorise expressions, either into primes or into coprime numbers. The following results are then often useful in solving problems:

- If a prime p is a factor of mn, then it is a factor of either m or n (or both). This is the definition of prime numbers on page 10.
- If a and b are coprime, then there exist integers x and y such that $xa + yb = 1$. This is theorem 1.2 on page 7.
- If a and m are coprime and a is a factor of mn, then a is a factor of n. This is theorem 1.3 on page 7.
- If M and N are coprime and MN is a perfect square, then M and N are perfect squares. This is theorem 1.9 on page 11.
- If M and N are coprime and a is a factor of MN, then there exist coprime integers b and c such that $a = bc$, where b is a factor of M and c is a factor of N. This is theorem 1.10 on page 12.

Problems in competitions often require the repeated use of these simple facts, and it pays to persevere since sometimes many steps are necessary before a solution is achieved.

Example 12.3 Let a and b be positive integers. Prove that if there exists an integer x such that b is a factor of $a^2x - a$, then there exists an integer y such that b is a factor of both $a^2y - a$ and $ay^2 - y$.

[BMO1 Mar 1984]

At first sight this is a daunting problem, since it seems very abstract and there are a lot of variables, so it is worthwhile spending some time making sure you know exactly what it means.

You have a couple of positive integers, and you can treat these as constants throughout. Now you are given a conditional statement: suppose that there is an integer x such that $b \mid (a^2x - a)$. There may be no such x, in which case there is nothing to prove, but that is unlikely, so a good starting point is to assume that one exists. You need to show that there is always another integer y such that $b \mid (a^2y - a)$ and $b \mid (ay^2 - y)$. Presumably it is possible to construct this new integer in some way from a, b and x, and you have to show how this is done.

The next step is to examine each of these divisibility statements and see if they have any immediate consequences, or if they are equivalent to some other statements. The first is that b is a factor of $a^2x - a$. It is always a good idea to factorise expressions, and in this case we see that $b \mid a(ax - 1)$. Now take a look at the two factors, and you will realise that they are coprime. This is because any (positive) common factor of a and $ax - 1$ will also divide into the linear combination $ax - (ax - 1) = 1$, so it can only be 1. This argument will turn out to be useful at several points in the proof. It now follows that, if b can be split into two factors, then one factor divides into each of a and $ax - 1$. Putting this into algebraic form, we can say that if $b = mn$, then $m \mid a$ and $n \mid (ax - 1)$. (Of course, b might be a prime, in which case one of m and n is 1, but this would be a very special case.) Moreover, since a and $ax - 1$ are coprime, so are m and n.

Whenever we obtain a fact like this, it never hurts to apply the Euclidean algorithm and deduce that there exist integers s and t such that $sm + tn = 1$. Recall that we are trying to construct a new integer y; it may turn out that this fact is useful in doing that.

Now we look at what properties this new integer should have. The first condition is that $b \mid (a^2y - a)$. We now know what we can deduce from this. Once again we have a coprime pair of factors a and $ay - 1$ and we also know that $m \mid a$; it follows that $n \mid (ay - 1)$. The other condition is that $b \mid (ay^2 - y)$ and a similar argument shows us that we need $m \mid y$.

Now take stock of where we are up to. We have positive integers m and n with

$$\begin{aligned} m &\mid a, \\ n &\mid (ax-1) \\ \text{and} \qquad sm + tn &= 1, \end{aligned}$$

and we need to create an integer y such that

$$\begin{aligned} n &\mid (ay-1) \\ \text{and} \qquad m &\mid y. \end{aligned}$$

The requirement that $n \mid (ay-1)$ looks rather hard to tie down, but if we combine it with the known fact that $n \mid (ax-1)$ we obtain a simpler requirement, namely $n \mid a(y-x)$. But n is coprime to a, so we can simplify this to $n \mid (y-x)$, or, equivalently, $y = x + kn$ for some integer k. Also, we need y to be a multiple of m. We have not yet made use of $sm + tn = 1$, and the crux of the proof is to realise that this is exactly what we need. Simply multiply through by x and rearrange, and we have $smx = x - tnx$. Now let $y = smx$; we now have a multiple of m which also satisfies $y = x + kn$ when $k = -tx$. The problem is now solved.

When you come to write this up neatly, you will leave out nearly all the investigational work you did in producing the solution. This is quite common in mathematics and it often disguises the stages which the solver has gone through and, in so doing, makes the eventual solution appear almost magical. Such a write-up might look like the following.

Suppose x is an integer such that $b \mid (a^2x - a) = a(ax-1)$. Since a and $ax - 1$ are coprime, there exist positive integers m and n such that $b = mn$, $m \mid a$ and $n \mid (ax-1)$. It follows that $(m, n) = 1$, so there exist integers s and t such that $sm + tn = 1$.

Let $y = smx = x - tnx$. Now

$$\begin{aligned} a^2y - a &= a(ax-1) + a^2(y-x) \\ &= a(ax-1) - a^2tnx \end{aligned}$$

But $b \mid a(ax-1)$ and $mn \mid an$ so $b \mid a^2tnx$; hence $b \mid (a^2y - a)$. Also

$$\begin{aligned} ay^2 - y &= y(ay-1) \\ &= smx\big(ax - 1 + a(y-x)\big) \\ &= smx(ax - 1 - atnx) \end{aligned}$$

and so $b = mn \mid (ay^2 - y)$. Hence y has the required properties.

Exercise 12b

1. The sum of all the factors of the positive integer n, including 1 but excluding n itself, is written as $S(n)$. If $S(n) > n$, then n is said to be *abundant*.

(a) Prove that if $n = pq$, where p and q are unequal primes, then n is not abundant.

(b) Prove that if m is abundant and p is a prime which is not a factor of m, then $S(pm) > (2+p)m$.

[Maclaurin 2003, adapted]

2. Determine the least possible value of the largest term in an arithmetic progression of seven distinct primes. *[BMO1 Dec 2004]*

3. If N is a positive integer, and there are exactly 2005 ordered pairs (x,y) of positive integers such that

$$\frac{1}{x} + \frac{1}{y} = \frac{1}{N}$$

prove that N is a perfect square. *[BMO2 Feb 2005]*

4. Show that there is exactly one pair of positive integers m, n, with $n < 200$, such that

$$\frac{59}{80} < \frac{m}{n} < \frac{45}{61}.$$

[BMO1 Nov 1987]

5. The integer m is at least 3 and $n = m^6 - 1$. Let p be a prime and k be a positive integer such that p^k is a factor of n. Prove that $p^{3k} < 8n$.

[BMO2 Jan 2010]

12.3 Harder problems

More sophisticated problems sometimes require the use of congruence arithmetic. In particular, the following techniques are often useful:

- quadratic residues—for example, squares cannot be $2 \pmod 3$;
- Fermat's little theorem (theorem 6.2 on page 45).

Example 12.4 Let $a_1 = 9$ and $a_{r+1} = 9^{a_r}$ for $r \geq 1$. Prove that the last two digits of a_3 written in base 10 are the same as the last two digits of a_4 written in base 10, and identify these digits. *[BMO1 Mar 1971]*

This problem is clearly asking us to work modulo 100 since we are only interested in the last two digits of the base 10 representation of numbers. It is worth looking first at the sequence of powers of 9, reduced modulo 100, which looks like this

$$09, 81, 29, 61, 49, 41, 69, 21, 89, 01, 09, \ldots$$

and it is clear that there is a cycle of length 10. In other words, if $r \equiv s \pmod{10}$, then $9^r \equiv 9^s \pmod{100}$.

We now begin to calculate the values of $a_r \pmod{100}$. Clearly $a_1 = 9$ and $a_2 = 9^9 \equiv 89 \pmod{100}$. So $a_2 = 100k + 89$, and

$$\begin{aligned} a_3 &= 9^{100k+89} \\ &= 9^{10(10k+8)} \times 9^9 \\ &\equiv 9^9 \pmod{100} \\ &\equiv 89 \pmod{100}. \end{aligned}$$

By exactly the same argument, all subsequent numbers in the sequence (a_i) are $89 \pmod{100}$ so the digits in question are 89.

The numbers in the sequence do, as you will notice, become astronomically large quite soon, so it is difficult to imagine any other approach to this question!

Some problems require careful analysis of cases. In the example which follows, the crucial steps concern residues with appropriate choices of base.

Example 12.5 For each integer $n > 1$, let $p(n)$ denote the largest prime factor of n. Determine all triples x, y, z of distinct positive integers such that

(i) x, y, z are in arithmetic progression, and
(ii) $p(xyz) \leq 3$.

[BMO2 Feb 2003]

The first condition gives the relationship $2y = x + z$, and the second tells us that the only prime factors involved in this question are 2 and 3. We shall assume, without loss of generality, that $x < y < z$ (since they are distinct), and we now look for common factors.

If the highest common factor of x and y is h, then h is also a factor of z, so we can remove this factor from all three numbers and call the positive integers which result a, b, c. It is now true that $2b = a + c$ and $a < b < c$, and we note that a and b are coprime (since we have removed their highest common factor), so b and c are also coprime. However, it is possible that a and c share a common factor of 2.

Now consider b, which contains only the prime factors 2 and 3. If it contains both of these, then both a and c are 1 (since they are coprime to b), and this is impossible since $a < b < c$. Similarly, b cannot be 1. Hence b is either a power of 2 or of 3. We now split into two cases.

If $b = 2^n$ for some $n > 0$, then $a = 3^\ell$ and $c = 3^m$, with $\ell < m$. Since a, c have a common factor of 1 or 2 it is immediate that $\ell = 0$ and $a = 1$. This implies that $3^m = 2^{n+1} - 1$. Looking at the sequence of powers of 2, reduced modulo 3, we see that $n + 1$ is even, and we now have

$$3^m = 2^{2k} - 1 = \left(2^k - 1\right)\left(2^k + 1\right).$$

The only two powers of 3 which differ by two are 1 and 3, so $k = 1$ and $m = 1$. We now have one solution $(a, b, c) = (1, 2, 3)$.

If, on the other hand, $b = 3^n$ for some $n > 0$, then $a = 2^\ell$ and $c = 2^m$, with $\ell < m$. Again the fact that a, c have a common factor of 1 or 2 means we have $\ell = 0$ or 1, and now parity considerations show that $\ell = 1$ and $a = 2$. We now obtain $3^n = 2^{m-1} + 1$. Again looking at powers of 2 modulo 3, we see that $m - 1 = 2k - 1$ is odd, and now we have $2^{2k+1} = 3^n - 1$. It is now useful to look at the sequence of powers of 3, reduced modulo 4, which alternate between 3 and 1. If $n = 1$, we obtain a solution $k = 0$, so $m = 2$ and $(a, b, c) = (2, 3, 4)$. If n is greater than 1 and odd, then $3^n - 1 \equiv 2 \pmod 4$ and hence cannot be a power of 2. So we need $n = 2t$ to be even, and now

$$2^{2k+1} = 3^{2t} - 1 = \left(3^t - 1\right)\left(3^t + 1\right)$$

but now we have powers of 3 differing by 2. The only solution is when $t = 1, n = 2, k = 1, m = 4$ and so $(a, b, c) = (2, 9, 16)$.

Putting back the highest common factor $h = 2^r 3^s$, we have three families of solutions for (a, b, c), namely

$$(h, 2h, 3h),\ (2h, 3h, 4h) \text{ and } (2h, 9h, 16h).$$

Sometimes you are asked to show that there are infinitely many pairs of numbers which satisfy a particular condition. The situation here is akin to that relating to Pell equations in example 8.2 on page 67. By trial, an initial solution to the equation was discovered and this was used to create a second solution. An iterative procedure was then used to give a third solution and, indeed, infinitely many more.

Example 12.6 Show that there are infinitely many pairs of positive integers (m, n) such that

$$\frac{m+1}{n} + \frac{n+1}{m}$$

is a positive integer. *[BMO2 Jan 2007]*

Let $\frac{m+1}{n} + \frac{n+1}{m} = k$. Without loss of generality, we can assume that $m \leq n$. First we investigate the possibility that $m = n$, and this gives us $k = \frac{2(n+1)}{n}$. Since n and $n + 1$ are coprime, the only possibilities are $n = 1, k = 4$ and $n = 2, k = 3$. So now we start looking for pairs with $m < n$, and immediately we find the example $(1, 2)$, again giving $k = 4$.

It is worth considering why there are two pairs giving $k = 4$ containing the same number 1. If we expand the defining relation, we obtain the Diophantine equation

$$m(m + 1) + n(n + 1) = 4mn.$$

Thinking of this as a quadratic in n, we have

$$n^2 + (1 - 4m)n + m^2 + m = 0 \tag{12.1}$$

Substituting $m = 1$, this gives the quadratic $n^2 - 3n + 2 = 0$ and $n = 1$ or 2, the two values we already know about. But now we can do the same thing assuming that $m = 2$, and obtain a new quadratic $n^2 - 7n + 6 = 0$ and $n = 1$ or 6. So another pair for (m, n) is $(2, 6)$. Again we substitute $m = 6$ to obtain a fourth pair $(6, 21)$.

In fact, we do not even need to find the quadratic to obtain this sequence, since the product of the roots at any stage is $m(m + 1)$. If we have a pair (a, b) satisfying equation (12.1), then the pair $\left(b, \frac{b(b+1)}{a}\right)$ also satisfies (12.1). This process now yields an infinite set of pairs, each giving the value $k = 4$; the first few terms are

$$(1,1),\ (1,2),\ (2,6),\ (6,21),\ (21,77),\ (77,286),\ (286,1066),\ldots$$

Equally well, we might have begun with $(2, 2)$ and obtained the sequence

$$(2,2),\ (2,3),\ (3,6),\ (6,14),\ (14,35),\ (35,90),\ (90,234),\ldots$$

which gives $k = 3$. We must, however, check that this process really does always produce a new term. Let two successive terms be (a, b) and (b, c) with $b > a$. From the sum of the roots of the quadratic (12.1), we have $a + c = 4b - 1$ and so $c - b = 3b - a - 1 > 0$. Hence the new term has $c > b$ as required.

Exercise 12c

1. Prove that, if n is a positive integer, then $3^n + 2 \times 17^n$ can never be a perfect square. *[BMO1 Jan 1991]*

2. Find, with proof, the smallest possible value of $|12^m - 5^n|$, where m and n are positive integers. *[BMO1 Mar 1981]*

3. Let n be an integer. Show that, if $2 + 2\sqrt{1 + 12n^2}$ is an integer, then it is a perfect square. *[BMO1 Dec 2006]*

4. Show that there is a positive integer N with the following properties:

(a) the binary expansion of N has precisely 2004 0s and 2004 1s;

(b) 2004 divides into N.

[BMO2 Feb 2004]

5. Determine the sequences $a_0, a_1, a_2, \ldots$ which satisfy all of the following conditions:

(a) $a_{n+1} = 2a_n^2 - 1$ for all $n \geq 0$,

(b) a_0 is a rational number, and

(c) $a_i = a_j$ for some i, j with $i \neq j$.

[BMO1 Dec 2008]

Chapter 13

Diophantine equations

A Diophantine equation is one in which only integer solutions are allowed. They have already appeared several times in this book: linear equations in section 1.4 on page 7 , quadratics in section 2.3 on page 19 and Pell equations in section 8.4 on page 67. Problems involving these can ask you to:

- find all the solutions (usually a finite list);
- show there are no solutions;
- show there are infinitely many solutions.

13.1 Divisibility and size arguments

Many equations can be solved by narrowing down the possible solutions to a list which it is feasible to check. Here the feasibility refers to the ability to check within the time frame of a competition without a calculator or computer!

Example 13.1 The magician Mij has 140 green balls and 140 red balls. To perform a trick, Mij places all the balls in two bags. In the black bag, there are twice as many green balls as red balls and in the white bag, the number of red balls is a multiple of the number of green balls. Neither bag is empty. Determine all the ways in which Mij can place the balls in the two bags in order to perform the trick. *[Maclaurin 2004]*

The obvious way forward is to let there be a red balls in the black bag and b green balls in the white bag. Then there are $2a$ green balls in the black bag and kb red balls in the white bag, where k is a positive integer. This leads us to the simultaneous equations

$$2a + b = 140$$
$$a + kb = 140.$$

Eliminating a gives $b = \frac{140}{2k-1}$. For b to be a positive whole number, we see that $2k - 1$ has to be a factor of 140, and indeed it has to be an odd factor since $2k - 1$ is odd. Hence the possible values of $2k - 1$ are $1, 5, 7$ or 35 and so k is $1, 3, 4$ or 18.

We now check that each of these values of k gives a solution, remembering that both a and b need to be positive integers. Substitution gives the following table:

k	a	b
1	0	140
3	56	28
4	60	20
18	68	4

Note the solution for $k = 1$ needs to be discarded since $a = 0$ means the black bag is empty, and this is not permitted by the question. The other solutions should all be checked and they work.

It is equally possible to solve the problem by eliminating b from the simultaneous equations to give

$$a = \frac{140k - 140}{2k - 1}.$$

This tells us that $2k - 1$ is a factor of $140k - 140$. However, since $140k - 140 = 70(2k - 1) - 70$ it follows that $2k - 1$ is a factor of $140k - 140$ if, and only if, it is a factor of 70. The solution then follows the same route as above.

This idea of 'dividing out' , that is, of writing

$$\frac{140k - 140}{2k - 1} = 70 - \frac{70}{2k - 1},$$

is very useful and will be used again and again.

Quite often we can limit the size of the variable we are looking at by using inequalities rather than factors, or indeed a mixture of both.

Example 13.2 Find all the integer solutions of the equation

$$n = \frac{m(3m+1)}{2m-1}.$$

We first note that m and $2m-1$ are coprime and so $2m-1$ divides into $3m+1$. However, we have

$$\frac{3m+1}{2m-1} = 1 + \frac{m+2}{2m-1}$$

and so we can limit the possible values of m by considering the behaviour of $\frac{m+2}{2m-1}$ for large values of $|m|$.

Clearly as $|m|$ increases in size, $\frac{m+2}{2m-1}$ approaches the value of $\frac{1}{2}$ and so eventually it cannot be an integer. Indeed if we solve the inequality

$$-1 < \frac{m+2}{2m-1} < 1, \qquad (13.1)$$

we can find limits for the value of m. This can be done either by drawing the graph of $y = \frac{m+2}{2m-1}$ or by noting that the inequality (13.1) is equivalent to $(m+2)^2 < (2m-1)^2$, which can be rewritten in the form $(m-3)(3m+1) > 0$. Thus (13.1) holds when $m > 3$ or $m < -\frac{1}{3}$ and so to find integer solutions to our equation we need only check $m = 0$, 1, 2, and 3. Since $m = 2$ gives a non-integer value of n we deduce that (m,n) is one of $(0,0)$, $(1,4)$ and $(3,6)$.

We must, however, remember to check the case $\frac{m+2}{2m-1} = 0$ separately. This gives us the extra solution pair $(-2,-2)$.

It is worth noting that this method works here because we know that $\frac{m+2}{2m-1}$ approaches a value between -1 and 1 as $|m|$ increases, which is why we considered this rather than $\frac{3m+1}{2m-1}$.

The following example is harder, but the essential technique is the same.

Example 13.3 Find all pairs of integers (x, y) such that

$$1 + x^2y = x^2 + 2xy + 2x + y.$$

[BMO2 Feb 2001]

We can view this either as a linear equation in y or as a quadratic equation in x. If we try the former, then we have

$$y\left(x^2 - 2x - 1\right) = x^2 + 2x - 1. \quad (13.2)$$

Since $x^2 - 2x - 1 = (x-1)^2 - 2$ is not zero for any integer (or indeed rational) x, we may rewrite equation (13.2) as

$$\begin{aligned} y &= \frac{x^2 + 2x - 1}{x^2 - 2x - 1} \\ &= 1 + \frac{4x}{x^2 - 2x - 1}. \end{aligned}$$

Now clearly $\frac{4x}{x^2-2x-1} = 0$ only when $x = 0$, and as x increases in size, $\frac{4x}{x^2-2x-1}$ eventually becomes between 1 and -1, in which case y cannot be an integer. This enables us to limit the possibilities for x.

Thus we need to solve the inequalities

$$-1 < \frac{4x}{x^2 - 2x - 1} < 1. \quad (13.3)$$

As in example 13.3, this can be done either by graph sketching or by replacing (13.3) with the equivalent inequality $16x^2 < \left(x^2 - 2x - 1\right)^2$. Using the difference between two squares, we can rewrite this in the form $\left(x^2 - 6x - 1\right)\left(x^2 - 2x - 1\right) > 0$. Thus (13.3) holds if

$$x < -1 - \sqrt{2}, \quad 3 - \sqrt{10} < x < -1 + \sqrt{2}, \quad \text{or} \quad 3 + \sqrt{10} < x.$$

Approximating $\sqrt{10}$ by 3 and $\sqrt{2}$ by 1.5, we deduce that to solve the original equation we need only check $x = -2, -1, 1, 2$, 3, 4, 5 and 6, out of which only -1 , 1, 2 and 3 work. Including the case $x = 0$ found above, we obtain the full set of solutions as

$$(x, y) = (-1, -1),\ (0, 1),\ (1, -1),\ (2, -7) \text{ or } (3, 7).$$

On occasions, a size argument by itself can work, if there are limits to the size that the variables are allowed to take.

Example 13.4 Prove that the equation $x^n + y^n = z^n$, where n is an integer greater than 1, has no solution for integer x, y and z for which $0 < x, y \leq n$. *[BMO1 March 1980]*

Since x and y are both non-zero, it follows that z is strictly greater than both x and y, that is, both x and y are less than or equal to $z - 1$. Thus $x^n + y^n \leq 2(z-1)^n$, but this could still be larger than z^n. So instead we need to concentrate on the larger of x and y and use the fact that we know they are both less than or equal to n. The fact that we also want to consider $(z-1)^n$ suggests we also want to try bounding with something which might appear as part of a binomial expansion. Thus, supposing $y \leq x \leq n$, we have

$$\begin{aligned} x^n + y^n &\leq x^n + x^n \\ &\leq x^n + nx^{n-1} \\ &\leq (z-1)^n + n(z-1)^{n-1}. \end{aligned}$$

These are the first two terms of the expansion of $(z - 1 + 1)^n$, that is, z^n and since $z - 1 > 0$ and $n > 1$ it follows that $(z-1)^n + n(z-1)^{n-1}$ is strictly less than z^n. Thus the equation has no solution.

Exercise 13a

1. Find all the right-angled triangles whose sides are positive integers and whose areas are equal to their perimeter.

2. Find all positive integers m, n, where n is odd, that satisfy

$$\frac{1}{m} + \frac{4}{n} = \frac{1}{12}.$$

[BMO1 Dec 2001]

3. Find all integers m, n satisfying $m^2 - 3mn - m + n = 0$.

[BMO1 Mar 1969]

4. Each of Paul and Jenny has a whole number of pounds.
He says to her: "If you give me £3, I will have n times as much as you."
She says to him: "If you give me £n, I will have 3 times as much as you."
Given that all these statements are true and n is a positive integer, what are the possible values for n? *[BMO1 Dec 2004]*

5. Find all solutions in positive integers x, y and z to the simultaneous equations

$$\begin{aligned} x + y - z &= 12 \\ x^2 + y^2 - z^2 &= 12. \end{aligned}$$

[BMO1 Dec 2007]

6. Show that the equation $m^2 + (m+1)^2 = n^4 + (n+1)^4$ has no solutions with m and n positive integers.

13.2 Following your nose

Experimentation can often be a useful way into a question. Sometimes it is a matter of putting in numbers until you get a feel for what is going on: constructing a table of values is never a waste of time as any clear pattern will usually be made clear from it.

At other times, it might be that you look at certain distinct classes of numbers first, for examples primes or simple product of primes. That can be particularly useful if the question involves limiting the number of factors, as in the next example.

Example 13.5 Determine a positive constant c such that the equation $xy^2 - y^2 - x + y = c$ has precisely three solutions (x, y) in positive integers. *[BMO1 Jan 1999]*

A lovely solution to this can be found to this in Geoff Smith's book [7]. Here, however, is a slightly more experimental answer.

As we are looking for a value of c, we just need to come up with one solution. This means that we can be more investigative in our approach. Factorising the expression seems a reasonable thing to do as we are looking for integer solutions, and indeed the equation can be rewritten as

$$x(y^2-1)-y(y-1)=c,$$

$$\text{or} \quad (y-1)[x(y+1)-y]=c.$$

Hence we have two integers $x(y+1)-y$ and $y-1$ which multiply to give c. Also $y>1$ since $c>0$. Hence we may assume that $y-1$ is strictly positive and so $x(y+1)-y$ is strictly positive as well. Thus we have two positive integers multiplying to give c and so both of them are factors of c. Hence presumably we do not want c to have too many factors.

Can c be prime? If so, we either have $x(y+1)-y=c$ and $y-1=1$, or $x(y+1)-y=1$ and $y-1=c$. Together these yield at most two solutions, $(x,y)=\left(\frac{c+2}{3},2\right)$ and $(1,\,c+1)$, and we need three. Hence c is not prime.

The next case we could consider is when c is a product of two primes, which are not necessarily distinct. If $c=p^2$, the square of a prime, then we have three possibilities:

1. $x(y+1)-y=p^2$ and $y-1=1$, giving $(x,y)=\left(\frac{p^2+2}{3},2\right)$;
2. $x(y+1)-y=1$ and $y-1=p^2$, giving $(x,y)=(1,\,p^2+1)$;
3. $x(y+1)-y=p$ and $y-1=p$, giving $(x,y)=\left(\frac{2p+1}{p+2},\,p+1\right)$.

Now the first two cases give integer solutions for any odd prime greater than 3, but the third has no solutions for p prime since we would require $p+2$ to be a factor of 3.

What, then, if $c=pq$, a product of two distinct primes? The same analysis gives:

1. $x(y+1)-y=pq$ and $y-1=1$, giving $(x,y)=\left(\frac{pq+2}{3},2\right)$;
2. $x(y+1)-y=1$ and $y-1=pq$, giving $(x,y)=(1,\,pq+1)$;
3. $x(y+1)-y=p$ and $y-1=q$, giving $(x,y)=\left(\frac{p+q+1}{q+2},\,q+1\right)$;

4. $x(y+1) - y = q$ and $y - 1 = p$, giving $y = p+1$ and $(x,y) = \left(\frac{p+q+1}{p+2}, p+1\right)$.

For this to work, we want exactly two out of

$$\frac{pq+2}{3}, \quad \frac{p+q+1}{q+2} \quad \text{and} \quad \frac{p+q+1}{p+2}$$

to be integers. We can now start a methodical search. The first choice $(p,q) = (2,3)$ does not work, but the next case $(p,q) = (2,5)$ does, giving solutions $(x,y) = (4,2)$, $(1,11)$ and $(2,3)$.
Thus 10 is a possible value for c.

At other times, just trying the obvious can help.

Example 13.6 Find all solutions in non-negative integers m, n to the equation $\sqrt{m} + \sqrt{n} = \sqrt{2009}$ *[BMO2 Jan 2009]*

About the only thing you can do is square the equation and the method works.

We have $\sqrt{m} = \sqrt{2009} - \sqrt{n}$ and so $m = 2009 + n - 2\sqrt{2009n}$. Since all the other terms are integers it follows that $\sqrt{2009n}$ is an integer, so $2009n$ is a perfect square. Since $2009 = 41 \times 7^2$ it follows that $41n$ is a perfect square, and so, as 41 is prime, $n = 41a^2$ for some positive integer a.

Similarly, $m = 41b^2$ for some positive integer b. Substituting back into the original, we obtain $b\sqrt{41} + a\sqrt{41} = 7\sqrt{41}$ and so $b + a = 7$. This gives $(a,b) = (0,7), (1,6), \ldots, (7,0)$ so

$$(m,n) = (0,2009),\ (41,1476),\ (164,1025) \text{ and } (369,656),$$

together with four more obtained by swapping m and n.

Exercise 13b

1. If n is a positive integer, find, with proof, all solutions of

$$\left\lfloor \sqrt[3]{1} \right\rfloor + \left\lfloor \sqrt[3]{2} \right\rfloor + \cdots + \left\lfloor \sqrt[3]{n^3 - 1} \right\rfloor = 400.$$

[BMO1 Mar 1975]

2. Find positive integers m and n such that

$$\left(\sqrt[3]{m}+\sqrt[3]{n}-1\right)^2 = 49+20\sqrt[3]{6}.$$

3. Prove that the equation $x^2+y^2 = z^5+z$ has infinitely many solutions with x, y and z being positive integers with no common factor greater than 1. *[BMO1 March 1985]*

13.3 Factorisation and the quadratic formula

Factorisation was useful in example 13.5 and can often help as was seen in chapter 2. In particular the factorisations in chapter 2 are worth learning.

Example 13.7 Find all integer solutions of the equation

$$m^3+8n^3 = 65.$$

Factorising gives

$$(m+2n)\left(m^2-2mn+4n^2\right) = 65$$

and so $m+2n = \pm 1$, ± 5, ± 13 or ± 65. Now

$$m^2-2mn+4n^2 = (m-n)^2+3n^2 \geq 0$$

and this tells us that $m+2n$ is positive. Now we have a list of four pairs of simultaneous equations which need to be checked. For example if $m+2n = 13$, then

$$(13-2n)^2-2n(13-2n)+4n^2 = 5,$$

which simplifies to $12n^2-78n+164 = 0$. This clearly has no integer solutions since 12 and 78 are divisible by 3 but 164 is not.

Repeating for the other three cases gives the only solution for (m,n) as $(1,2)$.

Modular arithmetic can often help, especially if we wish to show that an equation has no solutions, since it may be easier to show that the equation cannot work modulo a certain number, which means the equation has no solution. However the converse is not true: the fact that an equation has a solution modulo a certain number does not guarantee that the original equation has a solution.

Example 13.8 Show that the equation $x^2 = 3y^2 + 8$ has no integer solutions.

Since we have $3y^2$ on the right-hand side it makes sense to consider the equation modulo 3. Now we quickly get $x^2 \equiv 2 \pmod 3$, which is impossible since only 0 and 1 are quadratic residues (mod 3).

It is worth pointing out that if we had the equation $x^2 = 3y^2 + 7$, we would have reduced it to $x^2 \equiv 1 \pmod 3$, which does not tell us whether the original equation has a solution or not. However, if we look at the equation modulo 4 we get $x^2 \equiv 3$ or $2 \pmod 4$, so in fact this equation also has no solution, remembering again that only 0 and 1 are quadratic residues (mod 4).

Modular arithmetic is also particularly useful when the unknown is a power, as it often allows us to determine the parity of a given variable.

Example 13.9 Let m and n be positive integers with no prime factors greater than 5. Find all such m and n which satisfy $m^2 - n^2 = 2^k$ for some non-negative integer k. *[BMO2 Jan 2006]*

Factorising the given equation gives $(m-n)(m+n) = 2^k$ and hence $m - n = 2^a$ and $m + n = 2^b$, with a and b non-negative integers such that $a + b = k$ and $b > a$.

If $a = 0$, then m and n have opposite parity, which is impossible. Hence $b > a > 0$ and so $m = 2^{a-1} + 2^{b-1}$ and $n = 2^{b-1} - 2^{a-1}$. If $a > 1$, then both m and n are even, in which case we can reduce a and b by 1 and k by 2 to obtain another solution. Continuing in this way, we may therefore assume that $a = 1$. Hence $m = 2^{b-1} + 1$ and $n = 2^{b-1} - 1$, clearly both of which are odd.

Now m and n only have prime factors of 3 and 5, and differ by 2, so they cannot both have factors of 3 and 5. Thus either m is a power of 3 and n is a power of 5 or *vice versa*.

In the former case, we have $3^x = 2^{b-1} + 1$ and $5^y = 2^{b-1} - 1$. Then $2^{b-1} - 1 \equiv 1 \pmod 4$ and therefore $2^{b-1} \equiv 2 \pmod 4$. It follows that $b = 2$, $n = 1$ and $m = 3$. Thus we have solutions $(m, n) = (3 \times 2^p, 2^p)$ for some non-negative integer value of p.

In the latter case, we have $5^x = 2^{b-1} + 1$ and $3^y = 2^{b-1} - 1$. The first condition gives $2^{b-1} \equiv 0 \pmod 4$ immediately; this, together with the second condition, then gives $2^{b-1} \equiv 4 \pmod 8$ so that $b = 3$, $n = 3$ and $m = 5$. Hence we have solutions $(m, n) = (5 \times 2^p, 3 \times 2^p)$ where p is a non-negative integer.

The quadratic formula can also be useful if we wish to show a number needs to be a perfect square, by considering the discriminant.

Example 13.10 Prove that if x and y are rational numbers and

$$x^5 + y^5 = 2x^2y^2,$$

then $1 - xy$ is a perfect square.

If $x = 0$, then $y = 0$, and *vice versa*, in which case there is nothing to prove. Hence we can divide by x^2y^2 to obtain

$$x\left(\frac{x}{y}\right)^2 - 2 + y\left(\frac{y}{x}\right)^2 = 0.$$

Substituting $t = \left(\frac{x}{y}\right)^2$ reduces this to

$$xt - 2 + \frac{y}{t} = 0$$

and so

$$xt^2 - 2t + y = 0.$$

Thus the whole equation was a disguised quadratic! The discriminant is $4(1 - xy)$, which has to be a perfect square since t is rational. Thus $1 - xy$ is a perfect square.

The same method can be useful when we have an equation that is a quadratic in one variable: the discriminant can be used to limit the size of the other variable.

Example 13.11 Find all integer solutions to $x + y = x^2 - xy + y^2$.
The equation can be written as $x^2 - (y+1)x + y(y-1) = 0$. Considered as a quadratic in x, this has discriminant

$$\begin{aligned}(y+1)^2 - 4y(y-1) &= 1 + 6y - 3y^2 \\ &= 4 - 3(y-1)^2,\end{aligned}$$

which needs to be a perfect square. Since it cannot be greater than 4 the discriminant is either 0, 1 or 4, which gives $(y-1)^2 = 0$ or 1. Thus $y = 0, 1$ or 2. Substituting back into the original equation we obtain the possible values of x and the complete solution set $(x, y) = (0,0)$, $(0,1)$, $(1,0)$, $(1,2)$, $(2,1)$ and $(2,2)$.

Exercise 13c

1. (a) Find, with proof, all integer solutions of $a^3 + b^3 = 9$.

   (b) Find, with proof, all integer solutions of

$$35x^3 + 66x^2y + 42xy^3 + 9y^3 = 9.$$

[BMO1 Mar 1987]

2. Show that the equation $x(x+3) = 4y - 1$ has no integer solutions.

3. Determine all sets of non-negative integers x, y, z which satisfy the equation

$$2^x + 3^y = z^2.$$

4. Let p be an odd prime. Prove that there are unique positive integers x and y such that $x^2 = y(y+p)$, and give a formula for x and y in terms of p. *[BMO2 Feb 1992]*

5. Find all sets of integers which solve the equation $x^2 + xy + y^2 = x^2y^2$.

Solutions and commentary

Exercise 1a

1. $765 = 1 \times 630 + 135$, $630 = 4 \times 135 + 90$, $135 = 1 \times 90 + 45$, $90 = 2 \times 45$, so $(765, 630) = 45$.

2. $s = 14$, $t = 17$ and $17 = 1 \times 14 + 3$, so s and t are coprime.

   Now $st = 14 \times 17 = 238$. If $\frac{st}{n}$ is a common multiple of s and t where n is an integer, then both $\frac{s}{n}$ and $\frac{t}{n}$ must be integers. But $(s, t) = 1$, so $n = 1$ and hence $[s, t] = 238$.

   Now since s, t are coprime $(hs, ht) = h$ and $[hs, ht] = hst$. Putting $h = 45$ we get $[765, 630] = 45 \times 238 = 10\,710$.

3. $630 \times 765 = 481\,950 = 45 \times 10\,710$.

4. Yes and the proof follows exactly the steps used in the solution of questions 2 and 3.

5. From the text in section 1.3 on page 5, we know $(893, 705) = 47$. Now $893 = 47 \times 19$ and $705 = 47 \times 15$. But $(19, 15) = 1$ and $[19, 15] = 19 \times 15 = 285$. It follows that $[893, 705] = 47 \times 285 = 13\,395$.

6. (a) $x = -1 - 4k$, $y = 2 + 7k$, where k can be any integer.

   (b) $x = -1 + 12k$, $y = 3 - 35k$, where k can be any integer.

   (c) From theorem 1.4 there are no solutions since $(133, 84) = 7$, but 7 does not divide 1.

7. From theorem 1.4 h needs to be a multiple of 7. That $h = 7$ follows from the fact that $x = -5$, $y = 8$ does in fact provide a right-hand side of precisely 7.

8. For part (a), from the solution to question 6a note that $x = -1$, $y = 2$ satisfies the equation $7x + 4y = 1$, so if we wish to weigh an object of N g one can use the result $7Nx + 4Ny = N$ to deduce one possible result. Put the object with N 7 g weights making a total of $8N$ g in one pan, and then this can be balanced by $2N$ 4 g weights in the other pan. This means that if weights can be put in both pans then any whole number of grams can be weighed.

   For part (b) when weights can be put in one pan only to balance the given object in the other pan the answer is that objects of the following weights can be managed:

0 g, 4 g, 7 g, 8 g, 11 g, 12 g, 14 g, 15 g, 16 g and all integer weights greater than or equal to 18 g.

To see this, note that:

- 18 g can be managed with two 7 g weights and one 4 g weight;
- 19 g can be managed with one 7 g weight and three 4 g weights;
- 20 g can be managed with no 7 g weights and five 4 g weights;
- 21 g can be managed with three 7 g weights and no 4 g weights.

Thereafter adding an extra 4 g weight will take care of the cases 22 g, 23 g, 24 g, 25 g and so on by adding more 4 g weights.

Of course this will not be the most efficient way of performing the weighing, but one of the things to be learned about mathematics is that any correct method that works will do.

9. Use induction on n and theorem 1.4. If you are not familiar with the method of induction, see section 4.1 on page 29.

Exercise 1b

1. $244\,578\,251 = 23 \times 31 \times 37 \times 73 \times 127.$

   $944\,578\,251 = 3^2 \times 131 \times 733 \times 1093.$

   If you did this without using a software package such as *DERIVE* you will have seen how difficult it is to factorise large numbers into irreducibles and how long it takes. Techniques have been developed to speed up the process that depends on trying to divide by each irreducible in turn. However, the difficulty of the task for integers having 100 or more digits enables the arithmetic of such large numbers to be used in encryption.

2. $4061 = 31 \times 131$, $3813 = 3 \times 31 \times 41$, so $(4061, 3813) = 31$ and $[4061, 3813] = 499\,503$.

3. $(m, n) = p^2q^2r^3$, $[m, n] = p^4q^3r^4$. Both products are $p^6q^5r^7$.

4. Any factor of N has the form $p_1^{\beta_1} p_2^{\beta_2} \cdots p_n^{\beta_n}$, where $0 \le \beta_i \le \alpha_i$. Note that the factor 1 is chosen by setting all the β_i equal to 0. Since there are $\alpha_i + 1$ choices for each of the β_i, the result follows.

5. (a) An even number greater than 2 is equal to $2n$, for some $n > 1$, and so cannot be prime.

   (b) All integers are of the form $(6k \pm 2)$, $(6k \pm 1)$, $6k$, or $6k + 3$. The latter two are divisible by 3 and the first pair by 2, so the only possible primes greater than 3 are of the form $(6k \pm 1)$.

   If both $6k - 1$ and $6k + 1$ are prime for the same value of k like 17 and 19, they are said to be *twin primes*. Evidence suggests that not only are primes infinite in number, but that twin primes are infinite in number. Proving this is beyond the resource of mathematics at the present time.

6. Suppose that p is the largest prime number of the form $6k - 1$. Then consider the integer $N = p! - 1$. When N is factorised into primes suppose $N = p_1 p_2 p_3 \ldots p_k$. Then each of the primes p_j, $j = 1$ to k, is greater than p, for if not it would divide both N and $p!$ and hence would divide 1, which is impossible. Since p is the largest prime of the form $6k - 1$ it follows that all p_j are primes of the form $6k + 1$ and hence N, when divided by 6 leaves a remainder 1. But $N = p! - 1$, which has a remainder of 5 when divided by 6. The contradiction shows there is no largest prime number of the form $6k - 1$.

   A result due to Dirichlet, which is far beyond the scope of this book, is that if a and b are coprime then there are an infinite number of primes of the form $ak + b$.

7. General results of this kind do not exist, so it must be a particular case. If p is a prime greater than 3, then $p^2 + 2$, from the result of question 6, is equal to either $36k^2 - 12k + 3$ or $36k^2 + 12k + 3$ for some value of k. These are not prime. When $p = 2$ then $p^2 + 2 = 6$, which is not prime, so $p = 3$ is the only possibility, and then the three integers are 3, 11, 29 which are all prime.

8. Again using the result that all primes are of the form $p = 6k \pm 1$, $p^2 - 1 = 12k(3k \pm 1)$. Now if k is even there is obviously a factor of 24. And if k is odd $3k \pm 1$ is even. So in either case there is an extra factor of 2 to make $p^2 - 1$ divisible by 24.

   This result is true for all numbers of this form whether p is prime or not. So this result does not provide a test of whether a number is prime. We shall meet some tests for prime numbers later, but they are not very efficient.

9. Of the three integers $p, p+10, p+14$ if you divide them all by 3 you are bound to get one each of the remainders 0, 1, 2 (in some order). In other words one of them is divisible by 3. But they are all stated to be prime numbers. This is impossible unless $p = 3$.

10. If n is odd and greater than 1, then we may write $n = 2k+1$ for $k > 0$ and from the factorisation in question 2(d) of exercise 2b there is a factor $2+1 = 3$ and so $2^n + 1$ is not prime.

Project 1

The project asks you to find a formula in terms of a and b for the largest positive integer N which cannot be expressed in the form $N = xa + yb$, where both x and y are non-negative integers. Here a and b are coprime positive integers and without loss of generality you may take $a > b$.

Some of the evidence you might have collected is shown in table 14.1. It appears that a possible formula is $N = ab - a - b$. The proof is not easy,

a	b	N
5	2	3
5	3	7
5	4	11
6	5	19
7	2	5
7	3	11
7	4	17
7	5	23

Table 14.1

but if you have spotted the following clue you will not be surprised to know that the proof is based on it.

Look at the case $a = 7, b = 4$ given in the text. In the table on page 14 you will see the data shown in table 14.2. Each pair has one 'Yes' and one 'No'. Tabulate some of your other evidence and you will find the same. Of course, since a and b cannot both be even the proposed value of N is always odd, so this sort of pairing off is always possible. The main part of the argument is therefore the following result.

0	Yes	$\leftrightarrow$	17	No
1	No	$\leftrightarrow$	16	Yes
2	No	$\leftrightarrow$	15	Yes
3	No	$\leftrightarrow$	14	Yes
4	Yes	$\leftrightarrow$	13	No
5	No	$\leftrightarrow$	12	Yes
6	No	$\leftrightarrow$	11	Yes
7	Yes	$\leftrightarrow$	10	No
8	Yes	$\leftrightarrow$	9	No

Table 14.2

Lemma 14.1 *If m is a non-negative integer such that $0 \leq m \leq ab - a - b$, and $n = ab - a - b - m$, then precisely one of m, n is representable in the form $xa + yb$, where x and y are non-negative integers and the other is not so representable.*

PROOF Suppose in fact that $m = xa + yb$ and $n = ua + vb$. We want to disprove that all of x, y, u, v can be chosen to be non-negative. In fact we want to show that if x, y, u are non-negative then v is definitely negative. Now if x, y, u, v are non-negative then we have $0 \leq x \leq (b-1)$ and $0 \leq u \leq (b-1)$, otherwise m or n could get too large. Adding the two equations we get

$$m + n = ab - a - b = (x+u)a + (y+v)b.$$

That is,

$$ab = (x+u+1)a + (y+v+1)b \tag{14.1}$$

Now it follows from theorem 1.1 and the fact that a and b are coprime that $b \mid (x+u+1)$. But from the above inequalities

$$(x+u+1) \leq (2b-1) < 2b.$$

Hence $b = x+u+1$ and dividing equation (14.1) by b we get $y+v+1 = 0$. Thus, if y is non-negative, then v is negative. ❑

If you were convinced by that argument, then wake up! There is a hole in the proof. We have shown that small m and n cannot both be representable, but we have not shown that at least one of them is. Try to mend the proof yourself, and if necessary consult the full argument in *Challenges in Geometry* by C. J. Bradley, published by Oxford University Press.

Theorem 14.1 *For all integers $M > ab - a - b$ the equation $xa + ya = M$ has solutions in which x, y are non-negative.*

PROOF We are still assuming without loss of generality that $a > b$. Clearly none of $1, 2, 3, \ldots, b-1$ is representable, so, by lemma 14.1, $N-1$, $N-2$, $N-3$, $\ldots$, $N-b+1$ are all representable, where $N = ab - a - b$. By adding 1 to the value of y in each of these cases we may deduce that $N + b - 1$, $N + b - 2$, $N + b - 3$, $\ldots$, $N + 1$ are representable. $N + b$ is also representable, since $N + b = ab - a$ for which we may choose $x = (b-1)$, $y = 0$. We now have a sequence of b representable consecutive integers, namely $N + 1$, $N + 2$, $N + 3$, $\ldots$, $N + b$ and then by increasing the value of y by 1 again we get the next integers and so on. ❑

It is not an expectation that suddenly overnight you should be able to write mathematics of this level of sophistication. But it should be acknowledged that if general results are to be proved at all, then someone has to be able to do it and so it must be a reasonable aim that eventually you should be able to do so. What you should see about the above proof is that it is a generalisation of the particular case $a = 7$, $b = 4$. For the most part this is how algebraic results are established. Algebra without the benefit of study of particular cases is very seldom constructed. The danger with modern trends in the teaching of mathematics is that emphasis is placed in framing hypotheses, but not in proving them because of their difficulty. This book will have provided a service if you appreciate that making a conjecture of a result is often a very long way from proving it, and convincing the mathematical world of its veracity. Fermat conjectured his Last Theorem, but it was 300 years before Wiles proved it. And many interesting conjectures remain as open questions.

Exercise 2a

1. $(4x+5y)(4x-5y)$.
2. $(200+1)(200-1) = 201 \times 199 = 3 \times 67 \times 199$.
3. $2(4x+1)(2y-1)$.
4. $(x^2+y^2)(x^2-y^2) = (x^2+y^2)(x-y)(x+y)$.
5. $(x+7)(x+2)$.
6. $(x-7)(x-2)$.
7. $(x+7)(x-2)$.
8. $(x-7)(x+2)$.
9. $(2x+7y)(3x+2y)$.
10. $(3x-2y)(4x+3y)$.
11. $(3x-2y)(5x-3y)$.
12. $(2x-y)(7x+2y)$.

Exercise 2b

1. (a) $1000^2 - 3^2 = 1003 \times 997 = 17 \times 59 \times 997$.

   (b) By the result of question 4 of exercise 2a, $9984 = 10^4 - 2^4 = 104 \times 8 \times 12 = 2^8 \times 3 \times 13$.

   (c) Similarly $99\,999\,919 = 100^4 - 3^4 = 10\,009 \times 97 \times 103$.

   How much work do you have to do to show 10 009 is prime? The least sophisticated and most obvious method is to divide by each prime in turn starting with 2 then 3 then 5 and so on. Can you see why it is sufficient to stop when you have tried 97?

2. (a) $x^5 - y^5 = (x-y)(x^4 + x^3y + x^2y^2 + xy^3 + y^4)$.

   (b) $x^5 + y^5 = (x+y)(x^4 - x^3y + x^2y^2 - xy^3 + y^4)$.

   (c) $x^4 + 64 = (x^2+8)^2 - 16x^2 = (x^2 - 4x + 8)(x^2 + 4x + 8)$.

   (d) $x^{2k+1} + y^{2k+1} = (x+y)(x^{2k} - x^{2k-1}y + x^{2k-2}y^2 - \cdots + y^{2k})$.

(e) $x^{2k+1} - y^{2k+1} = (x - y)(x^{2k} + x^{2k-1}y + x^{2k-2}y^2 + \cdots + y^{2k})$.
Of course this may not be the complete factorisation. For example, $x^9 - y^9 = (x - y)(x^2 + xy + y^2)(x^6 + x^3y^3 + y^6)$.

3. $14\,640 = 11^4 - 1^4 = 10 \times 12 \times 122$.

4. $10\,064 = 10^4 + 64$, and by exercise 2b question 2(c) this comes to $68 \times 148 = 2^4 \times 17 \times 37$.

5. The terms in the sequence 1001, 1 000 001, 1 000 000 001, ... may be written in the form $(10^k)^3 + 1^3$, $k = 1, 2, 3, \ldots$ so by the factorisation in the text they are of the form $(10^k + 1)(10^{2k} - 10^k + 1)$, and hence they are not prime. For example,

$$\begin{aligned} 1001 &= 11 \times 91 = 11 \times 7 \times 13, \\ 1\,000\,001 &= 101 \times 9901, \\ 1\,000\,000\,001 &= 1001 \times 999\,001 = 11 \times 7 \times 13 \times 19 \times 52\,579. \end{aligned}$$

6. (a) $4^n - 1$ has a factor $(4 - 1)$ so $N(n)$ is always an integer.

(b) $N(4) = 5 \times 17$, $N(5) = 11 \times 31$, $N(6) = 3 \times 5 \times 7 \times 13$.

(c) Looking at small values of n suggests that $7 \mid N(n)$ if and only if n is a multiple of 3. Now

$$N(n) \equiv \tfrac{1}{3}(2^n - 1)(2^n + 1). \tag{14.2}$$

If $n = 3m$, then

$$N(n) = \tfrac{1}{3}(8^m - 1)(8^m + 1)$$

and it is clear that the first bracketed factor is divisible by 7.

If $n = 3m + 1$, then

$$N(n) = \tfrac{1}{3}(2 \times 8^m - 1)(2 \times 8^m + 1).$$

As $2 \times 8^m - 1 = 2(8^m - 1) + 1$, it is clear that the first bracketed term cannot have a factor of 7 and a similar argument works for the second bracketed factor.

The case $n = 3m + 2$ can be dealt with in the same way.

(d) If n is not a power of 2, then $n = 2^s m$, where s is a non-negative integer and m is an odd number greater than 1. The factorisation in equation 2.1 on page 15 shows that $2^m - 1$ is a factor of $2^n - 1$. For example,

$$2^{20} - 1 = (2^{10} + 1)(2^{10} - 1) = (2^{10} + 1)(2^5 + 1)(2^5 - 1).$$

Now if m is odd $2^m - 1$ is never divisible by 3, but it is of the form $4t + 3$ for some integer t, and so in its prime factorisation must contain an odd number of primes of the form $4k + 3$.

It can be shown that if $n = 2^s$, then $N(n)$ contains only prime factors of the form $4k + 1$.

Exercise 2c

1. The only possible factorisations of 80 in which both factors are even are 40×2, 20×4 and 10×8. These give solutions $(x, y) = (21, 19)$, $(12, 8)$ or $(9, 1)$.

2. If the edges are removed from the top and bottom and from both the left-hand and right-hand sides we are left with $m - 2$ rows and $n - 2$ columns. The data of the problem then means that

$$3(m - 2)(n - 2) = 2mn.$$

Multiplying out and rearranging this gives

$$mn - 6m - 6n + 12 = 0.$$

Factorising we get

$$(m - 6)(n - 6) = 24.$$

Since $24 = 24 \times 1 = 12 \times 2 = 8 \times 3 = 6 \times 4$ the following possibilities occur with $m > n$: $(m, n) = (30, 7), (18, 8), (14, 9), (12, 10)$.

3. From the answers to question 1 we have $(x, 2y) = (21, 19)$, $(12, 8)$ or $(9, 1)$. Hence $(x, y) = (12, 4)$.

4. $x^2 - 2y^2$ cannot be factorised over the integers. This equation is an example of a Pell equation (see section 8.4 on page 67).

Project 2

From exercise 1b question 10 we know that if n is odd them $2^n + 1$ is always divisible by 3. If n is even and not a power of 2, then we may write $n = (2k + 1)s$, where $s = 2^m$ for some values of $k > 0$ and $m > 0$. We then have $2^n + 1 = (2^s)^{2k+1} + 1$, which has a factor $2^s + 1$, and is therefore not prime. So $2^n + 1$ can only be prime if n is a power of 2. These numbers are called the *Fermat numbers* after Pierre de Fermat, who thought they might all be prime. He based his hypothesis on the slender evidence that they are prime for $n = 1, 2, 4, 8, 16$ when $2^n + 1 = 3, 5, 17, 257, 65\,537$ respectively. Later Euler showed that $2^{32} + 1 = 641 \times 6\,700\,417$, and it is now known that 2^{2^m} is not prime for $5 \leq m \leq 32$ and many larger values of m. At the time of writing (July 2010) 243 Fermat numbers are known to be composite and no other prime values have been found. For up-to-date information see [9]. The conjecture that has not yet been proved is that only a finite number of Fermat numbers are prime. A warning is now appropriate that *you should not frame a hypothesis on a small amount of evidence.*

There is a curious and beautiful link with geometry here. If a Fermat number is prime it is possible to perform a construction with a straight edge and compass when a regular polygon has that number of sides. So, for example, it is possible to find such a construction for a regular pentagon and a regular 17-sided polygon. This is an existence theorem. It is obvious that if a Fermat number greater than 65 537 is found to be prime no-one will ever perform the corresponding construction by hand.

Exercise 3a

1. $a = b + km$ and $b = c + lm$ gives $a = c + lm + km = c + (k + l)m$.

2. (a) $x \equiv 4 \pmod 7$.

   (b) $x \equiv 3$ or $7 \pmod 8$.

   (c) No solution since $6x \equiv 0 \pmod 3$.

   (d) $x \equiv 8 \pmod{11}$.

   (e) $x \equiv 0$ or $3 \pmod 6$.

3. No. $x = 3, y = 0$ is one counterexample.

4. Yes. If $5x \equiv 5y \pmod{15}$, then $5x - 5y = 15k$ hence $x - y = 3k$, so $x \equiv y \pmod 3$.

5. $2^6 = 64 \equiv -1 \pmod{13}$ and hence $2^{12} \equiv 1 \pmod{13}$.

6. If $8x \equiv 8y \pmod{12}$, then $8x - 8y = 12k$ so that $4x - 4y = 6k$ and $x - y \equiv 0 \pmod 3$. Conversely, if $x \equiv y \pmod 3$, then $x - y = 3k$ and $8x - 8y = 24k$ so $8x \equiv 8y \pmod{12}$.

   This generalises as follows: If $ax \equiv ay \pmod m$ and $(a, m) = h$, then $x \equiv y \pmod{\frac{m}{h}}$ and conversely.

   For suppose $a = kh$ and $m = lh$, where k, l are coprime, then $ax \equiv ay \pmod m \Rightarrow khx - khy = tlh \Rightarrow kx - ky = tl$. But k and l are coprime so $x - y = sl$ and $t = sk$ for some integer s. That is $x \equiv y \pmod l$ and $l = \frac{m}{h}$. The converse is straightforward.

7. $x \equiv 0 \pmod 3$.

Exercise 3b

1. (a) $x \equiv 3$ or $4 \pmod 7$.

   (b) $(x - 3)(x + 4) \equiv 0 \pmod{13}$. Hence $x \equiv 3$ or $9 \pmod{13}$.

2. $1, 4, 2$ are the quadratic residues (mod 7).

3. $1, 9$ are the quadratic residues (mod 16).

4. The only squares (mod 3) are 0 and 1.

5. An odd square is $1 \pmod 4$, hence the sum of two odd squares is $2 \pmod 4$, which is even. But all even squares are $0 \pmod 4$, and so the sum of two odd squares is never a square.

6. 0, 1, 2, 3, 4, 5, 6, 7, 8 (mod 9) when squared give respectively 0, 1, 4, 0, 7, 7, 0, 4, 1 (mod 9), so the only ways that three squares can be summed to give $0 \pmod 9$ are (0, 0, 0); (1, 4, 4); (1, 1, 7); (4, 7, 7) or permutations of these triples. In all cases there is a repeat, which means that $9 \mid (x^2 - y^2)$ or $9 \mid (y^2 - z^2)$ or $9 \mid (z^2 - x^2)$.

7. There are no solutions of $x^2 \equiv -1 \pmod{11}$.

   If $x^2 \equiv -1 \pmod{13}$, then $x \equiv 5$ or $8 \pmod{13}$.

   The conjecture is that $x^2 \equiv -1 \pmod p$, where p is an odd prime, has solutions if and only if p is of the form $4k+1$. A discussion of this will be found in the solution to question 4 of project 6 on page 162.

Exercise 3c

1. (a) $N = 100M + 10P + R \equiv 10P + R \pmod 4$. Hence N is divisible by 4 if, and only if, the number formed by its last two digits is divisible by 4.

   (b) Similarly, since 1000 is divisible by 8, an integer is divisible by 8 if, and only if, the number formed by its last three digits is divisible by 8.

2. (a) An integer is divisible by 3 if, and only if, its digital sum is divisible by 3. Since $10M + R \equiv M + R \pmod 3$ the proof is similar to the proof of the test of divisibility by 9 in example 3.3.

   (b) $10M + R \equiv 0 \pmod{11}$ if, and only if, $-M + R \equiv 0 \pmod{11}$. Continuing the process we discover the rule that an integer is divisible by 11 if, and only if, the sums of sets of alternate digits differ by $0 \pmod{11}$.

   Thus 574 904 is divisible by 11 since $5 + 4 + 0 \equiv 7 + 9 + 4 \pmod{11}$.

3. $10M + R \equiv 0 \pmod{31} \Leftrightarrow 30M + 3R \equiv 0 \pmod{31} \Leftrightarrow 3R - M \equiv 0 \pmod{31} \Leftrightarrow M - 3R \equiv 0 \pmod{31}$.

4. (a) One way is to use $10M + R \equiv 0 \pmod{17} \Leftrightarrow 50M + 5R \equiv 0 \pmod{17} \Leftrightarrow M - 5R \equiv 0 \pmod{17}$.

   (b) One way is to use $10M + R \equiv 0 \pmod{19} \Leftrightarrow 20M + 2R \equiv 0 \pmod{19} \Leftrightarrow M + 2R \equiv 0 \pmod{19}$.

5. $10M + R \equiv 0 \pmod{47} \Leftrightarrow 140M + 14R \equiv 0 \pmod{47} \Leftrightarrow M - 14R \equiv 0 \pmod{47}$.

   Using this relation repeatedly gives $5\,802\,432 \rightarrow 580\,243 - 28 = 580\,215 \rightarrow 58\,021 - 70 = 57\,951 \rightarrow 5795 - 14 = 5781 \rightarrow 578 - 14 = 564 \rightarrow 56 - 56 = 0$ and hence $5\,802\,432$ is divisible by 47.

Project 3

u	v	u^2	v^2	$x = 2uv$	$y = u^2 - v^2$	$z = u^2 + v^2$
5	2	25	4	20	21	29
5	4	25	16	40	9	41
6	1	36	1	12	35	37
6	5	36	25	60	11	61
7	2	49	4	28	45	53
7	4	49	16	56	33	65
7	6	49	36	84	13	85
8	1	64	1	16	63	65
8	3	64	9	48	55	73
8	5	64	25	80	39	89
8	7	64	49	112	15	113

For proof of the necessity of the parameter system for Pythagorean triples, we start from the point in the text where we stated with proof that one of x, y must be even and the other odd. So suppose that x is even and y is odd. Then $x^2 = (z - y)(z + y)$. Since z, y are odd, $z - y$, $z + y$ are even. If $2d$ is their highest common factor, $2d \mid (z - y)$ and $2d \mid (z + y)$. This means that $2d \mid 2z$ and $2d \mid 2y$ so, since y, z are coprime, $d = 1$. So each of $z - y$, $z + y$ is twice a perfect square. Writing $z + y = 2u^2$ and $z - y = 2v^2$, we find $x^2 = 4u^2v^2$ and $x = 2uv$, $y = u^2 - v^2$, $z = u^2 + v^2$.

The sufficiency of the parameter system follows from the algebraic identity

$$(2uv)^2 + \left(u^2 - v^2\right)^2 = \left(u^2 + v^2\right)^2.$$

1. Either $u \equiv 0$ or $v \equiv 0 \pmod 3$ in which case $3 \mid x$ or $(u, v) \equiv (1, 1)$, $(2, 2)$, $(1, 2)$, $(2, 1) \pmod 3$. In the first two cases $u - v \equiv 0 \pmod 3$ and in the second two cases $u + v \equiv 0 \pmod 3$. Then $u^2 - v^2 \equiv 0 \pmod 3$ and $3 \mid y$. Notice that $3 \mid z$ never occurs.

2. If $u \equiv 0$ or $v \equiv 0 \pmod 5$, then $5 \mid x$. If $u \equiv v \pmod 5$, then $u - v \equiv 0 \pmod 5$ and $5 \mid y$. If $u + v \equiv 0 \pmod 5$ then $5 \mid y$. This leaves the cases $(u, v) \equiv (1, 2), (2, 1), (1, 3), (3, 1), (2, 4), (4, 2), (3, 4), (4, 3) \pmod 5$ and in all these cases $u^2 + v^2 \equiv 0 \pmod 5$ and $5 \mid z$.

3. If $z = x + 1$, then $u^2 + v^2 = 2uv + 1$ and therefore $(u - v)^2 = 1$ and $u = v + 1$. Clearly there are an infinite number of such cases: the first three are the triples $(3, 4, 5)$, $(12, 5, 13)$ and $(24, 7, 25)$.

4. If $y = x + 1$, then $u^2 - v^2 = 2uv + 1$ and so $(u - v)^2 - 2v^2 = 1$. Putting $u - v = t$ we have $t^2 - 2v^2 = 1$. The first instance of this is $t = 3$, $v = 2$, $u = 5$, which is shown as the first entry in the table above. Hence we have

$$
\begin{aligned}
3^2 - 2 \times 2^2 &= (3 + 2\sqrt{2})(3 - 2\sqrt{2}) = 1 \\
t^2 - 2v^2 &= (t + v\sqrt{2})(t - v\sqrt{2}) = 1 \\
(3 + 2\sqrt{2})(t + v\sqrt{2}) &= (3t + 4v) + (3v + 2t)\sqrt{2} \\
(3 - 2\sqrt{2})(t - v\sqrt{2}) &= (3t + 4v) - (3v + 2t)\sqrt{2}
\end{aligned}
$$

   On multiplying these last two equations, we see that $T = 3t + 4v$, $V = 3v + 2t$ is also a solution of $t^2 - 2v^2 = 1$. The next instance is therefore $T = 17$, $V = 12$ giving $(u, v) = (29, 12)$ and the triple $(696, 697, 985)$.

   The equation $t^2 - 2v^2 = 1$ is an example of a Pell equation, and is further investigated in section 8.4 on page 67.

Finally you were asked to find all integer-sided right-angled triangles with perimeter 330. Now $x + y + z = 2ku(u + v)$, where k is any scale factor of enlargement. Hence $ku(u + v) = 165 = 3 \times 5 \times 11$. Also $u < u + v < 2u$. When $k = 1$ we have $u = 11$, $v = 4$. When $k = 3$ or 5 there are no solutions. When $k = 11$ we have $u = 3$, $v = 2$. The two possibilities, therefore, are $(x, y, z) = (88, 105, 137)$ or $(132, 55, 143)$.

Exercise 4a

1. $P(1)$ is true since $1^2 = \frac{1}{6}(1 \times 2 \times 3)$.

   If $P(k)$ is true then

$$\begin{aligned} 1^2 + 2^2 + \cdots + k^2 + (k+1)^2 &= \tfrac{1}{6}k(k+1)(2k+1) + (k+1)^2 \\ &= \tfrac{1}{6}(k+1)(2k^2 + k + 6k + 6) \\ &= \tfrac{1}{6}(k+1)(2k^2 + 7k + 6) \\ &= \tfrac{1}{6}(k+1)(k+2)(2k+3) \end{aligned}$$

   and hence $P(k+1)$ is true.

   And so $P(n)$ is true for all positive integers n by the principle of mathematical induction.

2. $P(1)$ is true since $\frac{1}{1\times 2} = \frac{1}{2} = \frac{1}{1+1}$.

   If $P(k)$ is true then

$$\begin{aligned} \frac{1}{1 \times 2} + \frac{1}{2 \times 3} + \cdots + \frac{1}{k(k+1)} + \frac{1}{(k+1)(k+2)} & \\ &= \frac{k}{k+1} + \frac{1}{(k+1)(k+2)} \\ &= \frac{1}{(k+1)(k+2)} \times (k^2 + 2k + 1) \\ &= \frac{k+1}{k+2} \end{aligned}$$

   and hence $P(k+1)$ is true.

   And so $P(n)$ is true for all positive integers n by the principle of mathematical induction.

3. $P(1)$ is true since $1^3 - 25 \times 1 = -24$ which is divisible by 6.

   If $P(k)$ is true then there exists an integer m such that

$$f(k) = k^3 - 25k = 6m.$$

Then

$$\begin{aligned} f(k+1) &= (k+1)^3 - 25(k+1) \\ &= 6m + 3k^2 + 3k + 1 - 25 \\ &= 6m - 24 + 3k(k+1). \end{aligned}$$

But $k(k+1)$ is the product of two consecutive integers and is therefore even. Hence $k(k+1) = 2s$ for some integer s. It follows that $f(k+1) = 6(m+s-4)$ and hence $P(k+1)$ is true.

And so $P(n)$ is true for all positive integers n by the principle of mathematical induction.

4. The correct conjecture is that $u_n = 2^n + 1$.

   $P(1)$ and $P(2)$ are true since $u_1 = 2 + 1 = 3$ and $u_2 = 2^2 + 1 = 4 + 1 = 5$.

   If $P(k-1)$ and $P(k)$ are true then $u_{k-1} = 2^{k-1} + 1$ and $u_k = 2^k + 1$. Then from the recurrence relation

$$\begin{aligned} u_{k+1} &= 3(2^k + 1) - 2(2^{k-1} + 1) \\ &= 2^{k-1}(6-2) + (3-2) \\ &= 2^{k+1} + 1 \end{aligned}$$

   and hence $P(k+1)$ is true.

   And so $P(n)$ is true for all positive integers n by the principle of mathematical induction.

Exercise 4b

1. For this sum $a = 1, d = 2, n = 50$ and so the answer is

$$25(2 + 49 \times 2) = 2500.$$

   It is probable that you knew beforehand that the sum of the first N odd numbers is N^2 for all positive integers N.

2. The terms in the first sequence are of the form $13 + 5n$ and those of the second sequence are of the form $7 + 6m$, where m and n are non-negative integers. We therefore require solutions of the equation $6m - 5n = 6$. From the theory of chapter 1 the general solution

of this equation is $m = 1 + 5t$, $n = 6t$ and so the common terms are of the form $13 + 30t$, for non-negative integers t.

3. The sum of all numbers between 1 and 3000 inclusive is $1500 \times 3001 = 4\,501\,500$. The sum of all even numbers between 2 and 3000 inclusive is $750 \times 3002 = 2\,251\,500$. The sum of all numbers divisible by 3 between 3 and 3000 inclusive is $500 \times 3003 = 1\,501\,500$. But in the last two categories we have counted numbers divisible by 6 twice so we must calculate their sum so that they are not subtracted twice. Their sum is $250 \times 3006 = 751\,500$. It follows that the sum of all integers between 1 and 3000 inclusive that are not divisible by 2 or 3 is

$$4\,501\,500 - 2\,251\,500 - 1\,501\,500 + 751\,500 = 1\,500\,000.$$

4. Since $1 + 2 + 3 + \cdots + k = \frac{1}{2}k(k+1)$ we have the sum of the consecutive integers

$$\begin{aligned}(m+1) + (m+2) + \cdots + (n-1) + n &= \tfrac{1}{2}n(n+1) - \tfrac{1}{2}m(m+1) \\ &= \tfrac{1}{2}(n-m)(n+m+1).\end{aligned}$$

Now one of $n - m$ and $n + m + 1$ is odd and the other is even, so this is an integer with an odd factor. It follows that all integers except powers of 2 can be expressed as the sum of two or more consecutive positive integers.

For example, if we wish to express 35 in this way then we require

$$(n-m)(n+m+1) = 70$$

and one solution is $n - m = 2$, $n + m + 1 = 35$ giving $n = 18$, $m = 16$ and

$$17 + 18 = 35.$$

Another solution is $n - m = 5$, $n + m + 1 = 14$ giving $n = 9$, $m = 4$ and

$$5 + 6 + 7 + 8 + 9 = 35.$$

Yet another solution is $n - m = 7$, $n + m + 1 = 10$ giving $n = 8$, $m = 1$ and

$$2 + 3 + 4 + 5 + 6 + 7 + 8 = 35.$$

(Note that $n - m = 1$ is not allowed since there have to be at least two terms in the sum.)

5. The sum to n terms is $2n^2 + 103n$. The smallest value of n for this to exceed 1 000 000 is $n = 682$ giving 1 000 494.

Exercise 4c

1. $a = 5$ and $r = 6$ so the sum is

$$5 \times \frac{6^{20} - 1}{6 - 1} = 6^{20} - 1.$$

2. $a = 9, r = -\frac{1}{3}$ so the sum is

$$9 \times \frac{1 - (\frac{1}{3})^{13}}{1 + \frac{1}{3}} = \frac{797\,161}{118\,098}.$$

Since $r^n \to 0$ as n increases indefinitely, the sum tends to

$$\frac{9}{\frac{4}{3}} = \frac{27}{4}.$$

3. We want to prove that if a and b are positive then $2\sqrt{ab} \leq (a + b)$. This follows since $(a^2 + 2ab + b^2) \geq 4ab$, which in turn comes from $(a - b)^2 \geq 0$.

4. We require the least value of n such that $5^n > 4\,000\,001$, which is $n = 10$.

Project 4

If p is prime then its only divisors are 1 and p, therefore $d(p) = 2$ and $\sigma(p) = p + 1$. Primes are characterised by either of these equations.

If $n = p^2$, where p is prime, then the divisors are 1, p and p^2, therefore $d(n) = 3$ and

$$\sigma(n) = 1 + p + p^2 = \frac{p^3 - 1}{p - 1}.$$

The only examples in the table in the text for when $d(n)$ is odd are 9, 49 and 100 and these are all when n is a perfect square. For an integer that is not a perfect square the divisors always pair off so that the product of the two in a pair equal n. For example, when $n = 6$ you get 1×6 and 2×3, and the number of divisors is four. But when n is a perfect square, there is one and only one divisor, namely $\sqrt{n}$, that partners itself. In such cases the number of divisors must therefore be odd. For example, when $n = 100$ you get 1×100, 2×50, 4×25, 5×100 and 10×10 , and the number of divisors is nine.

If $n = p^3$ then $d(n) = 4$ and $\sigma(n) = \frac{p^4-1}{p-1}$.

If $n = pq$, where p and q are distinct primes, then the four divisors are $1, p, q$ and pq, so that $d(n) = 4$ and $\sigma(n) = (1+p)(1+q)$.

If $n = pq^2$, then $d(n) = 6$ and $\sigma(n) = (1+p)(1+q+q^2)$.

If $n = p^2q^2$ then $d(n) = 9$ and $\sigma(n) = (1+p+p^2)(1+q+q^2)$.

All of these are particular cases of the general result for $n = p^k q^m$, for which the divisors are of the form $p^s q^t$ where $0 \le s \le k$ ($k+1$ values) and $0 \le t \le m$ ($m+1$ values), so their number is $d(n) = (k+1)(m+1)$. Their sum is equal to

$$(1+p+p^2+\cdots+p^k)(1+q+q^2+\cdots+q^m),$$

since this product contains as its terms each one of the $(k+1)(m+1)$ divisors. Using the formula for the sum of a geometric progression this can be simplified to

$$\sigma(n) = \frac{(p^{k+1}-1)(q^{m+1}-1)}{(p-1)(q-1)}.$$

The above analysis is easily extended to the case when n has more than two distinct prime factors. For example, when $n = 1008 = 2^4 \times 3^2 \times 7$ we have $d(1008) = 5 \times 3 \times 2 = 30$ and

$$\sigma(1008) = \frac{(2^5-1)(3^3-1)(7^2-1)}{(2-1)(3-1)(7-1)} = 31 \times 13 \times 8 = 3224.$$

The form of the general expressions for $d(n)$ and $\sigma(n)$ shows that they are both what are called multiplicative functions. A *multiplicative function* $m(n)$ is one for which $m(n_1 n_2) = m(n_1)m(n_2)$, whenever n_1 and n_2 are co-prime.

Now we give answers to the numbered questions.

1. The smallest positive integer with $d(n) = 6$ is 12, which beats the other possible candidates, which are 18 and 32.

2. $\sigma(n)$ is odd if and only if all its factors of the form

$$(1 + p + p^2 + \cdots + p^k)$$

are odd. When $p = 2$ this provides no restriction on k. But when p is an odd prime k must be even. In other words all odd primes must occur to an even power. Thus a necessary and sufficient condition for $\sigma(n)$ to be odd is that n is either a perfect square or twice a perfect square.

3. 28 is a perfect number. $28 = 2^2 \times 7$ so

$$\sigma(28) = (1 + 2 + 4)(1 + 7) = 7 \times 8 = 2 \times 28.$$

4. Consider now the integer $N = 2^{n-1}(2^n - 1)$, where $2^n - 1 = p$ is prime. We have

$$\sigma(N) = \sigma(2^{n-1}p) = (2^n - 1)(p + 1) = 2^n(2^n - 1) = 2^n p = 2N.$$

So when N is of this form it is perfect. For $n = 2, N = 6$ and for $n = 3, N = 28$. The next case is $n = 5$ and $N = 496$.

Primes of the form $2^n - 1$ are called *Mersenne primes* and it is thought that there are an infinite number of them. Of course $2^n - 1$ is composite if n is composite, so for a Mersenne prime n has to be prime. However, they are not frequent; for example, there are only 12 primes $n < 257$ for which one gets a Mersenne prime. At the time of writing (July 2010) there are 47 Mersenne primes known, the largest being $2^{43\,112\,609} - 1$, which has 12 978 189 digits. For up-to-date information see [8].

For every Mersenne prime there is an even perfect number. It is one of the unsolved problems of Number Theory whether an odd perfect number exists. Odd numbers up to about 10^{36} have been tested and none is perfect. Those who seek the record for finding the largest known prime number tend to search for Mersenne primes, because tests for their primality tend to be slightly easier to carry out than for other possible primes.

Exercise 5a

1. Suppose

$$n^2 = 1100a + 11b = 11(100a + b) = 11(99a + a + b).$$

Since n^2 is divisible by 11, it must be divisible by 11^2, which in turn means $11 \mid (a + b)$. But $0 < a + b < 19$, so $a + b = 11$. Now since n^2 is a square, b cannot be 2, 3, 7 or 8. Since $0 < a < 10$, b cannot be 0 or 1. Nor can $b = 5$, since then the square would end in 25, not 55. Now 5566 is not a square, and so $7744 = 88^2$ is the only possibility.

2. The sum of the squares from $n - 2$ to $n + 2$ inclusive is equal to $5(n^2 + 2)$. If this is a perfect square then $5 \mid (n^2 + 2)$, that is, $n^2 = 5m - 2$. But 3 is not a quadratic residue modulo 5. The contradiction establishes the result.

3. If $T_n = x^2$ for non-negative integers n and x we have

$$(2n + 1)^2 - 8x^2 = 1.$$

We now refer to section 8.4 on page 67, where the Pell equation

$$u^2 - 2v^2 = 1$$

is analysed. By considering this equation (mod 4), we see that the solutions are such that u is odd and v is even, so they are all suitable in this case. The first four are $(u, v) = (1, 0), (3, 2), (17, 12), (99, 70)$. These correspond to $(n, x) = (0, 0), (1, 1), (8, 6), (49, 35)$.

Exercise 5b

1. If $n = a^2 + b^2$, then $(a + b)^2 + (a - b)^2 = 2n$.

2. We already have $1378 = 33^2 + 17^2$. Using the second factorisation we also have $1378 = 37^2 + 3^2$.

3. $(1^2 + 2^2)(1^2 + 3^2) = 1^2 + 7^2 = 5^2 + 5^2 = 50$.

The next lowest comes from

$$(1^2 + 2^2)(2^2 + 3^2) = 1^2 + 8^2 = 4^2 + 7^2 = 65.$$

4. It gives $120^2 + 22^2 = 122^2 + 0^2$. Whenever $ax = by$ or $ay = bx$ the result degenerates and produces a Pythagorean triple.

5. The only cases are

$$\begin{aligned} 5 &= 1^2 + 2^2, & 13 &= 2^2 + 3^2, & 17 &= 1^2 + 4^2, & 29 &= 2^2 + 5^2, \\ 37 &= 1^2 + 6^2, & 41 &= 4^2 + 5^2, & 53 &= 2^2 + 7^2, & 61 &= 5^2 + 6^2, \\ 73 &= 3^2 + 8^2, & 89 &= 5^2 + 8^2, & 97 &= 4^2 + 9^2. \end{aligned}$$

Two points to note are

(i) that no prime of the form 3 (mod 4) is amongst them and
(ii) all expressions for primes of the form 1 (mod 4) are unique.

6. A perfect square is either 0 or 1 (mod 4), so that the sum of two perfect squares cannot be 3 (mod 4).

7. Four ways. A specific case illustrates all the necessary details. Since $5 = 1^2 + 2^2$, $13 = 2^2 + 3^2$ and $17 = 1^2 + 4^2$, we can use identities (5.1) and (5.2) to show that

$$5 \times 13 = (1^2 + 4^2)(2^2 + 3^2) = 1^2 + 8^2 \text{ and } 4^2 + 7^2$$

and we now have

$$\begin{aligned} & 5 \times 13 \times 17 = (1^2 + 8^2)(1^2 + 4^2) = 12^2 + 31^2 \text{ and } 4^2 + 33^2 \\ \text{and} \quad & 5 \times 13 \times 17 = (4^2 + 7^2)(1^2 + 4^2) = 32^2 + 9^2 \text{ and } 24^2 + 23^2. \end{aligned}$$

It is not difficult to generalise the result to cover the question of how many essentially different ways there are of expressing any integer as the sum of two squares.

Exercise 5c

1. We have

$$\begin{aligned} 4(T_m + T_n) + 1 &= 2m(m+1) + 2n(n+1) + 1 \\ &= (m+n+1)^2 + (m-n)^2. \end{aligned}$$

2. Use identity (5.3) with $m = a + b$ and either $n = a - b - 1$ or $n = b - a$, depending which is positive.

3. Suppose the integer $N = T_k + T_m + T_n$, then

$$8N + 3 = (2k+1)^2 + (2m+1)^2 + (2n+1)^2.$$

4. From question 3 we have

$$8N + 7 = (2k+1)^2 + (2m+1)^2 + (2n+1)^2 + 2^2.$$

5. (a) Suppose that $4(T_m + T_n) + 1 = (4k+1)^2$. Then

$$T_m + T_n = \tfrac{1}{4}\left((4k+1)^2 - 1\right) = 2k(2k+1) = 2T_{2k}.$$

   (b) Solving simultaneous equations yields

$$\begin{aligned} m &= a^2 - b^2 + 2ab + 2a, \\ n &= b^2 - a^2 + 2ab + 2b \\ \text{and} \quad k &= \tfrac{1}{2}(a^2 + b^2 + a + b) \\ &= T_a + T_b. \end{aligned}$$

   (c) We have $m = 355$, $n = 211$, $k = 146$, $u = 24$ and $v = 3$. The corresponding Pythagorean triple is $144^2 + 567^2 = 585^2$ and we also have $T_{355} + T_{211} = 2T_{292}$.

It is possible to show that every primitive Pythagorean triple has an equivalent form in which one triangular number is the mean of two others.

Project 5

1. Identity (5.1) follows by considering $(z^*w)(z^*w)^* \equiv (z^*z)(ww^*)$ and identity (5.2) from $(zw)(zw)^* \equiv (zz^*)(ww^*)$.

2. Simply multiply out term by term, but remember that the usual commutative laws of algebra do not hold.

3. We have

$$\begin{aligned} &(aE + uI + vJ + wK)(bE + xI + yJ + zK) \\ &\quad = (ab - ux - vy - wz)E + (ax + ub + vz - wy)I \\ &\qquad + (ay + vb + wx - uz)J + (az + wb + uy - vx)K. \end{aligned}$$

One can now verify that

$$\begin{aligned}(a^2+u^2+v^2+w^2)(b^2+x^2+y^2+z^2)\\ &= (ab-ux-vy-wz)^2+(ax+ub+vz-wy)^2\\ &\quad +(ay+vb+wx-uz)^2+(az+wb+uy-vx)^2,\end{aligned}$$

that is, $(PP^*)(QQ^*) = (PQ)(PQ)^*$.

This is a closure rule that says that the product of two expressions that are the sums of four integer squares is also the sum of four integer squares.

We know that primes of the form $1 \pmod 4$ are expressible as the sum of two integer squares, we know from questions 3 and 4 of exercise 5c that primes of the form $3 \pmod 8$ and $7 \pmod 8$ are expressible as the sums of three and four integer squares respectively. It follows by the closure relationship that all integers are expressible as the sum of no more than four integer squares. This theorem is attributed to Lagrange.

So although squares and triangular numbers are closely linked, there is the subtle difference in the representation of positive integers, in that only three triangular numbers are needed, whereas four squares are needed. It turns out that this means there is a slightly stronger result about the representation of integers as the sum of squares. This is that an odd integer is always expressible as the sum of four integer squares, where the integers involved may themselves be chosen to have a sum of 1. For example,

$$\begin{aligned} &27 = 4^2+(-3)^2+1^2+(-1)^2\\ \text{and}\quad &29 = (-4)^2+3^2+2^2+0^2.\end{aligned}$$

Exercise 6a

1. The tables are as follows.

   (a) Modulo 5:

×	1	2	3	4
1	1	2	3	4
2	2	4	1	3
3	3	1	4	2
4	4	3	2	1

   (b) Modulo 7:

×	1	2	3	4	5	6
1	1	2	3	4	5	6
2	2	4	6	1	3	5
3	3	6	2	5	1	4
4	4	1	5	2	6	3
5	5	3	1	6	4	2
6	6	5	4	3	2	1

   (c) Modulo 11:

×	1	2	3	4	5	6	7	8	9	10
1	1	2	3	4	5	6	7	8	9	10
2	2	4	6	8	10	1	3	5	7	9
3	3	6	9	1	4	7	10	2	5	8
4	4	8	1	5	9	2	6	10	3	7
5	5	10	4	9	3	8	2	7	1	6
6	6	1	7	2	8	3	9	4	10	5
7	7	3	10	6	2	9	5	1	8	4
8	8	5	2	10	7	4	1	9	6	3
9	9	7	5	3	1	10	8	6	4	2
10	10	9	8	7	6	5	4	3	2	1

2. In all cases with multiplication (mod p) with p prime, each residue in the answer table appears once and once only in each row and in each column. This is proved in theorem 6.1. Because the multiplica-

tion process is commutative ($ab = ba$) the table is symmetrical about the main diagonal. Numbers whose product is 1 are called *inverses*. For example, 7 and 8 are inverse (mod 11).

3. For the table (mod 5) we have for the smallest integer n for each m for which $m^n = 1$, $1^1 = 1$, $2^4 = 1$, $3^4 = 1$, $4^2 = 1$. As explained on page 46 this smallest integer n is called the order of m, and it is proved in theorem 6.3 that $n \mid (p-1)$.

4. The orders of 1, 2, 3, 4, 5, 6 (mod 7) are 1, 3, 6, 3, 6, 2 respectively. Note these are all divisors of 6.

5. The orders of the residues (mod 11) for 1, 2, 3, 4, 5, 6, 7, 8, 9, 10 are 1, 10, 5, 5, 5, 10, 10, 10, 5, 2 respectively, once more illustrating the remarks concerning divisibility.

Exercise 6b

1. In Proof 3 of Fermat's little theorem on page 45 the fact that p is prime is used in stating that the p cyclic permutations of a string are distinguishable from one another. If p is not prime this is not necessarily the case. For example, if $p = 6$ and $m = 2$ the 6 cyclic permutations of *ababab* are *ababab*, *bababa*, *ababab*, *bababa*, *ababab*, *bababa*, which fall into two lots of identical strings.

2. We prove 16 637 is composite by showing that

$$2^{16\,636} \not\equiv 1 \pmod{16\,637}.$$

We have

$$2^{14} = 16\,384 \equiv -253 \pmod{16\,637},$$

so

$$2^{28} \equiv 14\,098 \pmod{16\,637}.$$

Carrying on this way by squaring we get

$$2^{56} \equiv 8002 \pmod{16\,637}$$
$$2^{112} \equiv 12\,828 \pmod{16\,637}$$
$$2^{224} \equiv 1017 \pmod{16\,637}$$

$$\begin{aligned}
2^{448} &\equiv 2795 \pmod{16\,637}\\
2^{896} &\equiv 9272 \pmod{16\,637}\\
2^{1792} &\equiv 6605 \pmod{16\,637}\\
2^{3584} &\equiv 3811 \pmod{16\,637}\\
2^{7168} &\equiv -380 \pmod{16\,637}\\
2^{14\,336} &\equiv 11\,304 \pmod{16\,637}.
\end{aligned}$$

Now we may proceed as follows.

$$\begin{aligned}
2^{16\,128} &= 2^{14\,336} \times 2^{1792} \equiv 12\,701 \pmod{16\,637}\\
2^{16\,576} &= 2^{16\,128} \times 2^{448} \equiv 12\,574 \pmod{16\,637}\\
2^{16\,632} &= 2^{16\,576} \times 2^{56} \equiv 13\,209 \pmod{16\,637}\\
2^{16\,636} &\equiv 13\,209 \times 16 \equiv 11\,700 \pmod{16\,637}.
\end{aligned}$$

Note that $2^{16\,380} \equiv 1 \pmod{16\,637}$, a result that we refer to later.

This sort of calculation is fairly easy provided you use a spreadsheet with a MOD function. If you use a calculator to do the squaring, you may obtain $x \pmod{16\,637}$ from the simple algorithm

$$16\,637 \times \left(\frac{x}{16\,637} - \left\lfloor \frac{x}{16\,637} \right\rfloor\right),$$

where the symbol $\lfloor y \rfloor$ denotes the integer part of y. The larger the integer the more efficient the method is compared with dividing the integer by all primes less than its square root.

3. Since $x^{10} \equiv 1 \pmod{11}$, we need only solve $x^7 \equiv 5 \pmod{11}$ or $5x^3 \equiv 1 \pmod{11}$. Hence $x^3 \equiv 9 \pmod{11}$ since 5 and 9 are inverses. The cubes of the numbers $1, 2, 3, \ldots, 10 \pmod{11}$ are 1, 8, 5, 9, 4, 7, 2, 6, 3, 10 respectively. The solution is therefore $x \equiv 4 \pmod{11}$.

4. $9^2 \equiv 22 \pmod{59}$, so $9^4 \equiv 484 \equiv 12 \pmod{59}$, $9^8 \equiv 144 \equiv 26 \pmod{59}$, $9^{16} \equiv 676 \equiv 27 \pmod{59}$ and $9^{32} \equiv 729 \equiv 21 \pmod{59}$. It follows that $9^{50} \equiv 21 \times 27 \times 22 \equiv 25 \pmod{59}$.

Exercise 6c

1. $4! = 24 \equiv -1 \pmod 5$. Also $6! = 720 \equiv -1 \pmod 7$ and $10! = 3\,628\,800$, which on division by 11 gives 329 890 and remainder 10, so $10! \equiv -1 \pmod{11}$.

   Theorem 14.2 (Wilson's theorem) *For all primes p*

   $$(p-1)! \equiv -1 \pmod p.$$

   PROOF The case $p = 2$ is trivial, so we may suppose that p is an odd prime. First we ask the question: when is an element x, with $0 < x < p$, its own inverse? For this to be true we must have $x \equiv x^{-1} \pmod p$, that is $x^2 \equiv 1 \pmod p$. This implies $(x+1)(x-1) \equiv 0 \pmod p$. Since $0 < x < p$ this means $x = 1$ or $x = p - 1$. This means that of the elements from 2 to $p - 2$ inclusive they fall into $\frac{p-3}{2}$ pairs of *distinct* elements (a, b) such that $ab \equiv 1 \pmod p$. This means that the product of all these $p - 3$ elements is $+1 \pmod p$. Multiplying by 1 and $p - 1 \equiv -1 \pmod p$ we get $(p-1)! \equiv -1 \pmod p$. ❑

2. For each residue $a \pmod p$ we have $a^{p-1} \equiv 1 \pmod p$. This means that each of 1, 2, 3, ..., $p - 1$ is a solution of the equation $x^{p-1} \equiv 1 \pmod p$. But this equation is of a degree $p - 1$ so 1, 2, 3, ..., $p - 1$ exhaust the solutions of this equation. It follows by the remainder theorem that

   $$x^{p-1} - 1 \equiv (x-1)(x-2)(x-3)\cdots(x-p+1) \pmod p. \quad (14.3)$$

   For example, putting $p = 5$ we have

   $$\begin{aligned}(x-1)(x-2)(x-3)(x-4) &= x^4 - 10x^3 + 35x^2 - 50x + 24 \\ &\equiv x^4 - 1 \pmod 5.\end{aligned}$$

   Note that putting $x = 0$ in equation (14.3) provides another proof of Wilson's theorem.

3. We want to prove $a^{561} \equiv a \pmod{561}$ for all integers a such that $1 \le a < 561$. It is sufficient to prove that $a^{561} = a$ for the moduli 3, 11 and 17, since $561 = 3 \times 11 \times 17$ as a product of primes. For the first of these, simply note that $a \equiv 0, 1$, or $-1 \pmod 3$, so that

$a^{561} \equiv 0, 1, \text{ or } -1 \pmod 3$. For the second congruence, if $11 \mid a$ then both sides are $0 \pmod{11}$ and if 11 does not divide a we can use Fermat's little theorem to get $a^{561} = (a^{56})^{10}a \equiv a \pmod{11}$. For the third congruence, if $17 \mid a$ then both sides are $0 \pmod{17}$ and if 17 does not divide a we can use Fermat's little theorem to get $a^{561} = (a^{35})^{16}a \equiv a \pmod{17}$.

A Carmichael number is therefore one which gives the appearance of being a prime when tested by Fermat's little theorem. The method of proof provides a sufficient criterion for a positive integer m to be a Carmichael number. It must be odd, no prime p appearing in its prime factorisation must appear to a power greater than 1, and for each prime p appearing it must be the case that $(p-1) \mid (m-1)$. It can be proved that the criterion is also necessary and that there are an infinite number of Carmichael numbers. Despite this, testing for possible primality by using Fermat's little theorem is a very powerful tool and with minor modifications to overcome the problem of Carmichael numbers can be made into a foolproof test.

Project 6

1. $1^2 \equiv 1, 2^2 \equiv 4, 3^2 \equiv 2, 4^2 \equiv 2, 5^2 \equiv 4, 6^2 \equiv 1 \pmod 7$. It follows that $1, 2, 4$ are the three quadratic residues $\pmod 7$.

2. $1, 4, 9, 5, 3$ are the five quadratic residues $\pmod{11}$.
   $1, 4, 9, 3, 12, 10$ are the six quadratic residues $\pmod{13}$.
   $1, 4, 9, 16, 8, 2, 15, 13$ are the eight quadratic residues $\pmod{17}$.
   $1, 4, 9, 16, 6, 17, 11, 7, 5$ are the nine quadratic residues $\pmod{19}$.

3. It appears from the evidence in questions 1 and 2 that there are precisely $\frac{1}{2}(p-1)$ quadratic residues for a given odd prime p. This is in fact the case, as $x^2 \equiv y^2 \pmod p$ if and only if $x \equiv y$ or $x \equiv (p-y) \pmod p$.

4. -1 is a quadratic residue $\pmod p$ if and only if $p \equiv 1 \pmod 4$.

   We are looking for elements x such that $x^2 \equiv -1 \pmod p$. Such an element must satisfy $x^4 \equiv 1 \pmod p$, so the order of x is 4. (It cannot be 3 since $x^6 \equiv -1 \pmod p$.) Now by theorem 6.3 it follows that $4 \mid (p-1)$, so for such an element to exist it is necessary that $p \equiv 1 \pmod 4$.

It is also sufficient. By the assumption you are permitted to make, there is a primitive root g with order $p-1$. Since $p \equiv 1 \pmod 4$, we know that $q = \frac{p-1}{4}$ is an integer and we let $x = g^q$. Now, since $x^4 \equiv 1 \pmod p$ it follows that $x^2 \equiv \pm 1 \pmod p$. It cannot be 1, since the order of g would then be $\frac{p-1}{2}$, so $x^2 \equiv -1 \pmod p$, and hence -1 is a quadratic residue. This is the first step in proving that every prime of this form is expressible as the sum of two integer squares.

This assertion can also be proved using Wilson's theorem (page 161). Let $x = 1 \times 2 \times \cdots \times \frac{1}{2}(p-1)$. Then

$$(p-1)(p-2)\cdots\tfrac{1}{2}(p+1) \equiv (-1)^{\frac{p-1}{2}}\, x \pmod p.$$

So

$$(p-1)! \equiv (-1)^{\frac{p-1}{2}}\, x^2 \equiv x^2 \pmod p.$$

This in turn implies that

$$-1 \equiv \begin{cases} x^2 \pmod p \text{ if } p = 4k+1, \\ -x^2 \pmod p \text{ if } p = 4k+3. \end{cases}$$

5. We have $(x+4)^2 \equiv 2 \pmod{23}$. Hence $x + 4 \equiv 5$ or $18 \pmod{23}$. This means that $x \equiv 1$ or $14 \pmod{23}$.

Exercise 7a

1. $\phi(8) = 4$ since $1, 3, 5, 7$ are coprime to 8.

   $\phi(1) = 1$, $\phi(2) = 1$, $\phi(3) = 2$, $\phi(4) = 2$, $\phi(5) = 4$, $\phi(6) = 2$, $\phi(7) = 6$, $\phi(8) = 4$, $\phi(9) = 6$, $\phi(10) = 4$, $\phi(11) = 10, \phi(12) = 4$.

2. Obviously, since only 1 and p divide p, it follows that $\phi(p) = p - 1$.

3. The integers a, $1 \leq a \leq p^2$ that are not coprime with p^2 are p, $2p$, $3p, 4p, \ldots, p^2$ and are p in number. It follows that $\phi(p^2) = p^2 - p = p(p-1)$.

4. The positive integers less than 18 that are coprime to 18 are $1, 5, 7, 11$, 13, 17, so that $\phi(18) = 6$. Note that $5^6 \equiv 11^6 \equiv 7^3 \equiv 13^3 \equiv 17^2 \equiv 1 \pmod{18}$, so $a^6 \equiv 1 \pmod{18}$ in all cases.

Exercise 7b

1. From question 3 of exercise 7a, we have $\phi(25) = 20$. The powers of $2 \pmod{25}$ are 2, 4, 8, 16, 7, 14, 3, 6, 12, 24, so $2^{10} \equiv -1 \pmod{25}$. This means that 2 has order 20 (mod 25) and is therefore a primitive root. Other primitive roots are 8, 3, 12, 23, 17, 22 and 13.

   In fact there are $\phi(\phi(25))$ primitive roots. This is because in any cyclic group of order n generated by x, the order of x^k is $\frac{n}{(k,n)}$ for $0 \leq k < n$. The number of generators is thus $\phi(n)$. Applying this to G_n, of order $\phi(n)$, shows that, if there is a primitive root modulo n, there are $\phi(\phi(n))$ such roots.

2. (a) The elements of G_{24} are $1, 5, 7, 11, 13, 17, 19, 23$.

   (b) The table is as follows (mod 24).

$\times$	1	5	7	11	13	17	19	23
1	1	5	7	11	13	17	19	23
5	5	1	11	7	17	13	23	19
7	7	11	1	5	19	23	13	17
11	11	7	5	1	23	19	17	13
13	13	17	19	23	1	5	7	11
17	17	13	23	19	5	1	11	7
19	19	23	13	17	7	11	1	5
23	23	19	17	13	11	7	5	1

(c) $n = 2$. No, since all the elements are of order 2.

3. If there is a primitive root the argument used in proving Wilson's theorem on page 161 holds good and the product $M = -1$. Otherwise there may be elements of order 2 other than 1 and -1 as well as those that pair off with their inverses. In such cases it is clear that $M^2 = 1$, so that in all cases $M = 1$ or -1. Examples of $M = 1$ are when $m = 8, 12, 15$.

Exercise 7c

1. Those that are $5 \pmod 7$ are 5, 12, 19, 26, 33, ... and those that are $6 \pmod 9$ are 6, 15, 24, 33, ... so the solution appears to be $33 \pmod{63}$.

2. 367.

3. $6x \equiv 9 \pmod{15}$ means that $6x = 9 + 15k$ for integers k, so we can divide by 3 to get $2x \equiv 3 \pmod 5$, which in turn means $x \equiv 4 \pmod 5$. $3x \equiv 17 \pmod{44}$ means $3x \equiv 17 \pmod 4$ and $3x \equiv 17 \pmod{11}$. This in turn means that $x \equiv 3 \pmod 4$ and $x \equiv 2 \pmod{11}$. We now apply the Chinese remainder theorem with $a = 3, b = 2, m = 4, n = 11$. Now $cn \equiv 1 \pmod m$ gives $c = 3$ and $dm \equiv 1 \pmod n$ gives $d = 3$. Then $x = acn + bdm = 99 + 24 = 123 \equiv 35 \pmod{44}$. If we now want to solve the congruences simultaneously we need to use the Chinese remainder theorem on the two congruences $x \equiv 4 \pmod 5$ and $x \equiv 35 \pmod{44}$, the solution of which is $x \equiv 79 \pmod{220}$.

Exercise 7d

1. $\phi(15) = 8 = 2 \times 4 = \phi(3)\phi(5)$.

2. $5x \equiv 7 \pmod 8$ implies $x \equiv 3 \pmod 8$ and $2x \equiv 1 \pmod 3$ implies $x \equiv 2 \pmod 3$. Using the notation of the text we have $a = 3$, $b = 2$, $m = 8$, $n = 3$. Now $cn \equiv 1 \pmod m$ gives $c = 3$ and $dm \equiv 1 \pmod n$ gives $d = 2$. One solution is therefore $x_0 = anc + bdm = 27 + 32 = 59$, so the general solution is $x \equiv 11 \pmod{24}$.

3. The eight solutions are $t \pmod{15}$ according to the following table.

j	k	t
1	1	1
1	2	7
1	3	13
1	4	4
2	1	11
2	2	2
2	3	8
2	4	14

The eight values of t are the eight positive integers less than 15 that are coprime to 15.

4. $d(p^k) = k+1$ for a prime p and $d(p^k q^l) = (k+1)(l+1) = d(p^k)d(q^l)$ for two distinct primes p and q etc. The multiplicative property of the function d now follows by expressing m and n in terms of their prime factors. Similar considerations hold for the function σ.

Exercise 7e

1. $\phi(37) = 36$, since 37 is prime.

   $\phi(464) = 224$, since $464 = 2^4 \times 29$, so that $\phi(464) = 8 \times 28$.

   $\phi(2560) = 1024$, since $2560 = 2^9 \times 5$, so that $\phi(2560) = 2^8 \times 4$.

2. From the multiplicative property of ϕ we have

$$\begin{aligned}\phi(m) &= (p^a - p^{a-1})(q^b - q^{b-1})\cdots(w^k - w^{k-1}) \\ &= p^a q^b \cdots w^k \left(1 - \frac{1}{p}\right)\left(1 - \frac{1}{q}\right)\cdots\left(1 - \frac{1}{w}\right) \\ &= m\left(1 - \frac{1}{p}\right)\left(1 - \frac{1}{q}\right)\cdots\left(1 - \frac{1}{w}\right).\end{aligned}$$

For $m = 1000$ this gives $\phi(m) = 1000 \times \frac{1}{2} \times \frac{4}{5} = 400$.

3. $\phi(1\,000\,000) = 1\,000\,000 \times \frac{1}{2} \times \frac{4}{5} = 400\,000$.
Hence $3^{400\,001} \equiv 3 \pmod{1\,000\,000}$.

4. $\phi(m) = 10$ when $m = 11$ and $m = 22$.

5. $\phi(m) = \frac{1}{2}m$ so

$$\left(1 - \frac{1}{p}\right)\left(1 - \frac{1}{q}\right)\cdots\left(1 - \frac{1}{w}\right) = \frac{1}{2},$$

which occurs only when $m = 2^a$, for some positive integer a.

6. $\phi(9) = 6$ so

$$221^{333} \equiv 221^3 \equiv 5^3 \equiv 8 \pmod{9}.$$

Project 7

1. $\sigma(2^{n-1}p) = \sigma(2^{n-1})\sigma(p) = (2^n - 1)\sigma(p)$ so $(2^n - 1)\sigma(p) = 2^n p$. Hence $2^n - 1 \mid 2^n p$ so, since $2^n - 1, 2^n$ are coprime, $2^n - 1 \mid p$.

2. If $p = k(2^n - 1)$ then $(2^n - 1)\sigma(p) = 2^n k(2^n - 1)$ gives $\sigma(p) = k\,2^n$. But if $k > 1$ then $1, k, k(2^n - 1)$ are factors of p, so

$$\sigma(p) \geq 1 + k + k(2^n - 1) = 1 + k\,2^n,$$

a contradiction.

3. Since $k = 1$ we have $\sigma(p) = 2^n = p + 1$, so $p = 2^n - 1$ is prime.

4. It is enough to show that $p^r q^s$ is not perfect for primes p, q. This is because

$$\begin{aligned}
\sigma(p^r q^s) &= \sigma(p^r)\sigma(q^s) \\
&= \frac{p^{r+1}-1}{p-1} \times \frac{q^{s+1}-1}{q-1} \\
&< \frac{p^{r+1}q^{s+1}}{(p-1)(q-1)} \\
&= p^r q^s \times \frac{p}{p-1} \times \frac{q}{q-1} \\
&\leq p^r q^s \times \frac{3}{2} \times \frac{5}{4} \\
&< 2p^r q^s.
\end{aligned}$$

Exercise 8a

1. If $\frac{a}{b}$ and $\frac{c}{d}$ are rational numbers then so are

$$\frac{a}{b} + \frac{c}{d} = \frac{ad + bc}{bd}$$

$$\text{and} \quad \frac{a}{b} \times \frac{c}{d} = \frac{ac}{bd}$$

since if a, b, c, d are integers then so are $ad + bc$, ac and bd; also, provided b and d are both non-zero, then bd is non-zero. Note the importance of proving the denominator is non-zero when proving a number is rational.

2. That the arithmetic mean of two rational numbers is rational follows immediately from question 1. As the arithmetic mean of two distinct rational numbers p and q lies between them, it follows that the sequence of numbers p_n for $n \geq 1$, defined by $p_n = \frac{1}{2}(p_{n-1} + q)$ with $p_1 = \frac{1}{2}(p + q)$, are all distinct rationals between p and q.

3. (a) Use proof by contradiction: if x is rational, it is clear that x^n is also rational.

   (b) Again, use proof by contradiction.

4. Following the same method as proof 2 of theorem 8.1, we obtain $m^2 = 3n^2$. The left-hand side has an even number of prime factors and the right-hand side has an odd numbers of prime factors, giving a contradiction.

   If we try to apply same method to $\sqrt{4}$ we get $m^2 = 4n^2$; both sides now have an even number of prime factors so that no contradiction arises.

5. If N is not a perfect square, then it has at least one prime factor p which occurs an odd number of times in the factorisation of N. However, following the same method as in the proof of question 4, we have $m^2 = Nn^2$. The left-hand side has an even number of factors of p and the right-hand side has an odd number of factors of p, so we have a contradiction.

6. If they are in an arithmetic sequence, there exist non-zero integers n and m such that
$$n(\sqrt{5}-\sqrt{2}) = m(\sqrt{3}-\sqrt{2}).$$
So
$$n\sqrt{5} - m\sqrt{3} = (n-m)\sqrt{2}.$$
Squaring both sides and rearranging implies $\sqrt{15}$ is rational, which is a contradiction.

7. If $\sqrt{2}+\sqrt{3}$ were rational, squaring would imply $\sqrt{6}$ were rational, giving a contradiction. To show $\sqrt{2}+\sqrt{3}$ is algebraic, square the equation $x = \sqrt{2}+\sqrt{3}$ twice to get $x^4 - 10x^2 + 1 = 0$.

8. Consider the number of factors of 2 on each side of the equation $m^3 = 2n^3$.

9. If N is not a perfect nth power, then N has a prime factor p which appears k times in the prime factorisation of N, where k is not a multiple of n. Now if $x = \frac{a}{b}$, count the number of factors of p on both sides of $a^n = Nb^n$.

10. No; for example, $1+\sqrt{2}$ and $1-\sqrt{2}$ are both irrational but their sum and product are rational.

11. Without loss of generality we can assume that the integers are n and $n+1$. Then $\sqrt{n(n+1)}$ lies between them and is irrational by question 9. Alternatively, consider $n+\sqrt{\frac{1}{2}}$, for example.

12. Multiplying both rationals by their common denominator reduces the problem to question 11.

13. Let $r \neq 0$ be rational and s irrational. Suppose $r+s=t$ is rational, then $s = t-r$ is rational, since it is the difference of two rational numbers. Contradiction establishes the result. Similarly, if $rs = t$ is rational, than $s = \frac{t}{r}$ is rational, and so on.

14. Yes. Take, for example, $x = 2-\sqrt{3}$ and $x = 2-\sqrt{2}$ respectively.

15. $\log_{10} N = x \Leftrightarrow N = 10^x$, so if $x = \frac{p}{q}$ is rational, then $N^q = 10^p$ and therefore, comparing prime factorisations of both sides, N can only be a power of 10. If not, x is irrational.

16. A careful graph of $h(x) \equiv 2^x - x^2$ shows that there are three roots, namely 2, 4 and one between -1 and 0.

    Suppose this root is rational, and let it be $-\frac{p}{q}$ for positive coprime integers p, q. Prove that $2^p p^{2q} = q^{2q}$ and now use a parity argument to show that both p and q are even, which is a contradiction.

17. Either $s = \sqrt{2}^{\sqrt{2}}$ is rational or, if it is irrational, then $s^{\sqrt{2}} = 2$ is rational. Whether s is rational or not we still have a solution to the problem.

    In fact, it turns out that s is a transcendental number; this is a consequence of the Gelfond-Schneider theorem, which was proved in 1934.

Exercise 8b

1. (a) Substitution gives

$$\frac{p_{n+1}}{q_{n+1}} = \frac{p_n + 2q_n}{p_n + q_n}.$$

   It is easy to see that if $d \mid p_n + 2q_n$ and $d \mid p_n + q_n$, then $d \mid p_n$ and $d \mid q_n$. Hence if p_n and q_n are coprime, then so are $p_n + 2q_n$ and $p_n + q_n$. Thus $p_{n+1} = p_n + 2q_n$ and $q_{n+1} = p_n + q_n$.

   (b) Substitution gives $p_{n+1}^2 - 2q_{n+1}^2 = -(p_n^2 - 2q_n^2)$, and hence the result follows by induction.

   (c) The identity in (b) gives

$$x_n^2 - 2 = \frac{(-1)^n}{q_n^2}.$$

   It is clear that $q_n \to \infty$ as $n \to \infty$ and so $x_n^2 \to 2$. Therefore $x_n \to \sqrt{2}$ since $x_n > 0$.

2. $x^2 = 5$ gives $(x - 2)(x + 2) = 1$ so

$$x = 2 + \frac{1}{x+2} = \frac{2x+5}{x+2}.$$

The rest of the solution follows the same method as question 1.

3. $\dfrac{643}{430}$.

4. $\dfrac{633\,420\,529}{362\,200\,163}$.

Exercise 8c

1. By inspection $(u, v) = (2, 1)$ is a solution. Using the process in example 8.2 gives $(7, 4)$, $(26, 15)$, $(97, 56)$ as the next three pairs.

2. The cosine rule rearranged gives
$$(2c)^2 - 3b^2 = (2a - b)^2.$$
If $b = 2a$, then b and c cannot both be integers (unless they are both zero in which case there is no triangle), and we can divide both sides by $(2a - b)^2$. Setting
$$u = \frac{2c}{2a - b} \quad \text{and} \quad v = \frac{b}{2a - b}$$
in the first two sets of solutions for question 1 we get two triangles. The first solution gives us $a = b = c$, which is the equilateral case. The second solution gives us $5b = 8a$, so we can set $a = 5$ and $b = 8$, giving $c = 7$.

3. We need to solve $\frac{1}{2}n(n + 1) = m^2$ for integer n and m. Multiplying by 8 and completing the square we obtain $(2n + 1)^2 - 2(2m)^2 = 1$ and so we have the Pell equation from example 8.2 on page 67. Thus we will have infinitely many solutions if we can show the sequence of solutions generated there always have (using the same notation as the example) u_n odd and v_n even. But this follows by induction from the iterative formulae and the starting values of $u_1 = 3$ and $v_1 = 2$.

4. The question is equivalent to finding integer m and n such that
$$2(1 + 2 + 3 + \cdots + m) = 1 + 2 + 3 + \cdots + n$$
and so using the formula for the sum of an arithmetic progression, we have $m(m + 1) = \frac{1}{2}n(n + 1)$. Rearranging in a similar way to question 3 we get
$$u^2 - 2v^2 = -1, \tag{14.4}$$

where $u = 2n + 1$ and $v = 2m + 1$. Now $(u, v) = (1, 1)$ is a solution by inspection, and we can generate further solutions as follows. We know $(3, 2)$ is a solution to the equation with -1 replaced by 1 so if (u, v) satisfies equation (14.4) then

$$(u^2 - 2v^2)(3^2 - 2 \times 2^2) = -1$$

and so

$$(3u + 4v)^2 - 2(2u + 3v)^2 = -1$$

(using the same method as in section 8.4 on page 67). Thus, starting with our solution above, we can keep generating new ones as usual and a similar induction shows that u and v will always be both odd, giving integer solutions for n and m.

Project 8

1. (a) $\frac{765}{630} = [1; 4, 1, 2]$.
   (b) $\frac{430}{259} = [1; 1, 1, 1, 16, 1, 1, 2]$.

2. Every rational number can be represented as a finite continued fraction in precisely two different ways. These two representations agree except in their final terms. In the longer representation the final term in the continued fraction is 1; the shorter representation drops the final 1, but increases the new final term by 1.

   For example, $\frac{8}{5} = [1; 1, 1, 1, 2]$ or $[1; 1, 1, 1, 1, 1]$.

3. $\sqrt{2} = [1; 2, 2, 2, \ldots]$, where all the entries after the first one are 2. This clearly satisfies the equation

$$x = 1 + \frac{1}{1 + x},$$

   which simplifies to $x^2 = 2$. The procedure used in producing it is the same as that described in example 8.1 on page 64, and the terms in the sequence (x_n) derived there are the result of truncating the infinite continued fraction.

4. This satisfies $x = 1 + \frac{1}{x}$, which reduces to the quadratic equation $x^2 - x - 1 = 0$. The positive root is the golden ratio $\frac{1}{2}(1 + \sqrt{5})$.

5. $\pi = [3; 7, 15, 1, 292, \ldots]$.

   The large number 292 means that $[3; 7, 15, 1] = \frac{355}{113}$ is a good rational approximation to π.

Continued fractions for irrationals are clearly infinite. It can be shown that the truncation method always produces, in some sense, a sequence of best rational approximations to the irrational.

Continued fractions can be used to investigate a large number of results in number theory, such as the solution of Diophantine equations, the theory of the Pell equation and quadratic residues.

If you want to find out more about continued fractions, see [2].

Exercise 9a

1. For the middle inequality, use algebra to show that

$$b_{n+1} - a_{n+1} = \frac{(a_n - b_n)^2}{2(a_n + b_n)} > 0;$$

the two outside inequalities quickly follow from this.

Since (b_n) is decreasing and bounded below, the sequence converges to a limit L. Now $a_n = 2b_{n+1} - b_n$ and hence (a_n) converges to L as well. Finally, $a_n b_n = N$ so that $L^2 = N$.

2. This time it is not easy to identify the limit. It was Gauss who spotted that it is, in fact,

$$\frac{\pi}{2\int_0^{\frac{\pi}{2}} \frac{d\theta}{\sqrt{a_1^2 \sin^2\theta + b_1^2 \cos^2\theta}}}.$$

3. (a) $\dfrac{y^{n+1} - x^{n+1}}{y - x} = y^n + y^{n-1}x + \cdots + yx^{n-1} + x^n$, where there are $n+1$ terms on the right-hand side, each between and x^n and y^n.

   (b) Use the right-hand inequality in (9.1).

   (c) The required inequality is equivalent to

$$\left(1 - \frac{1}{n}\right)^n < \left(1 - \frac{1}{n+1}\right)^{n+1},$$

   which comes from the left-hand inequality in (9.1).

   (d) $a_{n+1} < b_{n+1}$ is clear from $b_{n+1} = \left(1 + \frac{1}{n+1}\right) a_{n+1}$. The bounds for the common limit come from $a_1 = 2$ and $b_5 = 1.2^6 < 3$.

4. (a) $c_n = (1 - \frac{1}{2}) + (\frac{1}{2} - \frac{1}{3}) + \cdots + (\frac{1}{n} - \frac{1}{n+1}) = 1 - \frac{1}{n+1}$ by cancellation of the inner terms.

   (b) (d_n) is increasing since $d_{n+1} = d_n + \frac{1}{(n+1)^2}$ and

$$\begin{aligned} d_n &< \frac{1}{1^2} + \frac{1}{1 \times 2} + \cdots + \frac{1}{n(n-1)} \\ &= 1 + c_{n-1} \\ &\leq 2, \end{aligned}$$

by (a). The limit for (d_n) is not obvious: it was Euler who first showed it to be $\frac{\pi^2}{6}$.

(c) (e_n) is increasing since $e_{n+1} = e_n + \frac{1}{(n+1)!}$ and

$$\begin{aligned} e_n &< 1 + \frac{1}{1!} + \frac{1}{1 \times 2} + \cdots + \frac{1}{n(n-1)} \\ &= 2 + c_{n-1} \\ &\leq 3, \end{aligned}$$

by (a). The binomial expansion gives

$$\begin{aligned} a_n &= \left(1 + \frac{1}{n}\right)^n \\ &= 1 + \frac{n}{n} + \frac{1}{2!}\frac{n(n-1)}{n^2} + \frac{1}{3!}\frac{n(n-1)(n-2)}{n^3} + \cdots + \frac{1}{n!}\frac{n!}{n^n} \\ &< 1 + 1 + \frac{1}{2!} + \frac{1}{3!} + \cdots + \frac{1}{n!} \\ &= e_n. \end{aligned}$$

It follows that $\lim_{n\to\infty} a_n \leq \lim_{n\to\infty} e_n$. [Why can we not say $\lim_{n\to\infty} a_n < \lim_{n\to\infty} e_n$?] In fact the limits are equal, and equal to the important mathematical constant e.

Exercise 9b

1. (a) $0.35 = \dfrac{35}{100} = \dfrac{7}{20}$.

   (b) $0.862\,75 = \dfrac{86\,275}{100\,000} = \dfrac{3451}{4000}$.

2. (a) $\dfrac{19}{20} = \dfrac{95}{100} = 0.95$.

   (b) $\dfrac{19}{160} = \dfrac{11\,875}{100\,000} = 0.118\,75$.

3. (a) If $x = 0.\dot{4}$ then $10x = 4.\dot{4}$ and $9x = 4$, so $x = \frac{4}{9}$.

   (b) If $x = 0.\dot{4}\dot{5}$ then $100x = 45.\dot{4}\dot{5}$ and $99x = 45$, so $x = \frac{5}{11}$.

   (c) If $x = 0.\dot{4}5\dot{9}$ then $1000x = 459.\dot{4}5\dot{9}$ and $999x = 459$, hence $x = \frac{17}{37}$.

(d) If $x = 0.6\dot{4}5\dot{9}$ then $x = \dfrac{6}{10} + \dfrac{17}{370} = \dfrac{239}{370}$.

(e) $\dfrac{538\,461}{999\,999} = \dfrac{7}{13}$.

(f) $0.6\dot{3} = \dfrac{6}{10} + \dfrac{3}{90} = \dfrac{19}{30}$.

(g) $0.5\dot{0}3\dot{7} = \dfrac{5}{10} + \dfrac{37}{9990} = \dfrac{68}{135}$.

(h) $0.237\,5\dot{4}3\,\dot{2} = \dfrac{2375}{10\,000} + \dfrac{432}{9\,990\,000} = \dfrac{87\,891}{370\,000}$.

4. The denominator has to divide exactly into 10^n for some integer $n \geq 1$. In other words the denominator must only have 2s and 5s as factors. Then and only then can the fraction be converted into an equivalent one with a power of 10 in the denominator, and hence written down as a decimal that terminates. For example, the multiplier for $\frac{19}{160}$ is $5^4 = 625$.

Exercise 9c

1. $\frac{1}{13} = 0.\dot{0}76\,92\dot{3}$ and $\frac{2}{13} = 0.\dot{1}53\,84\dot{6}$.

2. For $\frac{1}{13}$ the successive remainders are 10, 9, 12, 3, 4, 1 and for $\frac{2}{13}$ they are 7, 5, 11, 6, 8, 2. Note that between the two of them all the twelve non-zero remainders of 13 get used. It is shown later in the book that the period of a recurring decimal for $\frac{1}{p}$, where p is an odd prime, is a divisor of $p - 1$.

3. $0.\dot{3} \times 0.\dot{5} = \dfrac{1}{3} \times \dfrac{5}{9} = \dfrac{5}{27} = \dfrac{185}{999} = 0.\dot{1}8\dot{5}$.

   There is obviously scope here for an interesting investigation as to whether one can learn to do arithmetic (addition, subtraction, multiplication, and division) with recurring decimals without changing into fractions and changing back afterwards. Can one predict the period in terms of the periods of the data?

4. The period is always three. They fall into twelve sets of three in which the digits cycle:

$$\frac{1}{37} = 0.\dot{0}2\dot{7} \qquad \frac{10}{37} = 0.\dot{2}7\dot{0} \qquad \frac{26}{37} = 0.\dot{7}0\dot{2}$$

$$
\begin{array}{lll}
\frac{2}{37} = 0.\dot{0}5\dot{4} & \frac{20}{37} = 0.\dot{5}4\dot{0} & \frac{15}{37} = 0.\dot{4}0\dot{5} \\
\frac{3}{37} = 0.\dot{0}8\dot{1} & \frac{30}{37} = 0.\dot{8}1\dot{0} & \frac{4}{37} = 0.\dot{1}0\dot{8} \\
\frac{5}{37} = 0.\dot{1}3\dot{5} & \frac{13}{37} = 0.\dot{3}5\dot{1} & \frac{19}{37} = 0.\dot{5}1\dot{3} \\
\frac{6}{37} = 0.\dot{1}6\dot{2} & \frac{23}{37} = 0.\dot{6}2\dot{1} & \frac{8}{37} = 0.\dot{2}1\dot{6} \\
\frac{7}{37} = 0.\dot{1}8\dot{9} & \frac{33}{37} = 0.\dot{8}9\dot{1} & \frac{34}{37} = 0.\dot{9}1\dot{8} \\
\frac{9}{37} = 0.\dot{2}4\dot{3} & \frac{16}{37} = 0.\dot{4}3\dot{2} & \frac{12}{37} = 0.\dot{3}2\dot{4} \\
\frac{11}{37} = 0.\dot{2}9\dot{7} & \frac{36}{37} = 0.\dot{9}7\dot{2} & \frac{27}{37} = 0.\dot{7}2\dot{9} \\
\frac{14}{37} = 0.\dot{3}7\dot{8} & \frac{29}{37} = 0.\dot{7}8\dot{3} & \frac{31}{37} = 0.\dot{8}3\dot{7} \\
\frac{17}{37} = 0.\dot{4}5\dot{9} & \frac{22}{37} = 0.\dot{5}9\dot{4} & \frac{35}{37} = 0.\dot{9}4\dot{5} \\
\frac{18}{37} = 0.\dot{4}8\dot{6} & \frac{32}{37} = 0.\dot{8}6\dot{4} & \frac{24}{37} = 0.\dot{6}4\dot{8} \\
\frac{21}{37} = 0.\dot{5}6\dot{7} & \frac{25}{37} = 0.\dot{6}7\dot{5} & \frac{28}{37} = 0.\dot{7}5\dot{6}
\end{array}
$$

For example,

$$\frac{3}{37} = 0.\dot{0}8\dot{1}$$

so

$$\frac{30}{37} = 10 \times 0.\dot{0}8\dot{1} = 0.\dot{8}1\dot{0}$$

and

$$\frac{300}{37} = 10 \times 0.\dot{8}1\dot{0} = 8.\dot{1}0\dot{8}$$

and subtracting 8 gives $\frac{4}{37} = 0.\dot{1}0\dot{8}$. This sort of behaviour always happens.

5. For (a), (b), (c), we have to show the pattern in the decimal expansions cannot eventually consist of repeating blocks of digits of a fixed

size. This follows because, in each case, eventually there appears an arbitrarily long block of zeroes. For (d), the binary expansion of the given number looks like (a) and we can use exactly the same argument (in binary rather than base 10).

Exercise 9d

1. $99\,999\,999 = 3^2 \times 11 \times 73 \times 101 \times 137$, so $\frac{1}{73}$, $\frac{1}{101}$ and $\frac{1}{137}$ have period 8.

   $999\,999\,999 = 3^4 \times 37 \times 333\,667$, so $\frac{1}{333\,667}$ has period 9.

   $9\,999\,999\,999 = 3^2 \times 11 \times 41 \times 271 \times 9091$, so $\frac{1}{9091}$ has period 10.

2. $21 = 3 \times 7$ so the period of $\frac{1}{21}$ is the LCM of 1 and 6, namely 6.

   $451 = 11 \times 41$ so the period of $\frac{1}{451}$ is the LCM of 2 and 5, namely 10.

   $429 = 3 \times 11 \times 13$ so, using an obvious generalisation, the period of $\frac{1}{429}$ is the LCM of 1, 2 and 6, namely 6.

Project 9

1. We begin with $\frac{1}{7} = 0.\dot{1}42\,85\dot{7}$, so $\frac{10}{7} = 1.\dot{4}28\,57\dot{1}$ and $\frac{3}{7} = 0.\dot{4}28\,57\dot{1}$.

   Similarly, we have $\frac{2}{7} = 0.\dot{2}85\,71\dot{4}$, $\frac{6}{7} = 0.\dot{8}57\,14\dot{2}$, $\frac{4}{7} = 0.\dot{5}71\,42\dot{8}$ and $\frac{5}{7} = 0.\dot{7}14\,28\dot{5}$, noting that if we continue the process we are back to where we started.

   The numerators form a sequence $1, 3, 2, 6, 4, 5, 1, 3, \ldots$, which is a geometric progression with first term 1 and common ratio 10, reduced modulo 7.

2. This time we begin with $0.\dot{0}58\,823\,529\,411\,764\,\dot{7}$ and the cycle of numerators goes

$$1, 10, 15, 14, 4, 6, 9, 5, 16, 7, 2, 3, 13, 11, 8, 12.$$

3. Starting from $\frac{1}{13} = 0.\dot{0}76\,92\dot{3}$, we obtain a cycle with numerators 1, 10, 9, 12, 3, 4. Note that, since the period of the decimal is 6, not 12, this is bound to happen. If we begin with $\frac{2}{13} = 0.\dot{1}53\,84\dot{6}$, we obtain a second cycle with numerators 2, 7, 5, 11, 6, 8.

4. The decimal $\frac{1}{239}$ has period 7, so we would expect to get 34 cycles of length 7.

5. If we start without any preconceptions, we might let $x = a \times 10^n + b$, where a is a single digit and b is an integer with n digits. Hence $3x = 10b + a$, so $7b = a(3 \times 10^n - 1)$.

   If $a = 7$, then $b = 3 \times 10^n - 1$, but this number is too long, since it has $n + 1$ digits.

   Hence we could let $a = 1$ and $7 \mid 3 \times 10^n - 1$, so $n = 5$ and $b = 42\,857$, giving the solution 142 857.

   However, there is a second solution: setting $a = 2$ we have $7 \mid 6 \times 10^n - 2$ and $b = 85\,714$, giving the solution 285 714.

   The fact that we are looking for solutions to a congruence such as $3 \times 10^n - 1 \equiv 1 \pmod 7$ suggests that this is related to the recurring decimal for $\frac{1}{7}$ and to the sequence in question 1.

6. This time we look at the sequence in question 1 backwards, and note that there is now a unique solution 142 857. It would be possible to devise similar problems with other primes, but we would need to allow leading zeros in integer representations.

Exercise 10a

1. $a(1 + rx + r^2x^2 + \cdots) = \dfrac{a}{1 - rx}$, provided $|x| < \frac{1}{r}$.

2. Provided $|x| < 1$,

$$a + (a+d)x + (a+2d)x^2 + \cdots = \frac{a}{1-x} + \frac{dx}{(1-x)^2} = \frac{a + (d-a)x}{(1-x)^2}.$$

3. $a_0 = 3, a_1 = 8, a_{n+2} = 2a_{n+1} - a_n, n \geq 0$.

4. $a = 3, d = 5$, so from question 2

$$f(x) \equiv \frac{3 + 2x}{1 - 2x + x^2}.$$

The recurrence relation is $a_{n+2} - 2a_{n+1} + a_n = 0$ and the same coefficients $1, -2, 1$ appear in the denominator of the generating function.

Exercise 10b

1. (a) $\dfrac{2}{2x-3} + \dfrac{3}{3x-2}$.

   (b) $2 + \dfrac{8}{x^2 - 4} = 2 + \dfrac{2}{x-2} - \dfrac{2}{x+2}$.

   (c) $\dfrac{2}{(x+1)^2} - \dfrac{3}{2x^2 + 2x + 1}$.

   (d) $\dfrac{1}{9(x-2)} + \dfrac{1}{3(x-2)^2} - \dfrac{1}{9(x+4)}$.

Exercise 10c

1. $f(x) \equiv \dfrac{2x}{(1-2x)^2} = 2x + 8x^2 + 24x^3 + 64x^4 + \cdots + (n2^n)x^n + \cdots$
so a_n is a power of 2 when n is a power of 2.

2. $\alpha + \beta = 2, \alpha\beta = -2$ and $(1 - \alpha x)(1 - \beta x) = 1 - 2x - 2x^2$. It follows that the recurrence relation is $a_{n+2} = 2(a_{n+1} + a_n)$.

3. $1 + 2x + 3x^2 + \cdots = (1-x)^{-2}$. Multiply by x and differentiate to obtain $1 + 2^2x + 3^2x^2 + \cdots = \dfrac{1+x}{(1-x)^3}$.

   So $x + 2^2x^2 + 3^2x^3 + \cdots = \dfrac{x(1+x)}{(1-x)^3}$.

   The third-order linear recurrence relation is

$$a_{n+3} = 3a_{n+2} - 3a_{n+1} + a_n,\ n \geq 0,$$
$$a_0 = 0,\ a_1 = 1,\ a_2 = 4,\ a_3 = 9.$$

   Putting $x = \frac{1}{2}$ in the generating function, the sum of the series is 6.

4. $a = 1, b = 3, c = 2, d = -2$ so the generating function is

$$f(x) \equiv \frac{1+x}{1-2x+2x^2}.$$

   Putting this into partial fractions you get

$$f(x) \equiv \frac{\frac{1}{2}(1-2i)}{1-\sqrt{2}xe^{\frac{i\pi}{4}}} + \frac{\frac{1}{2}(1+2i)}{1-\sqrt{2}xe^{-\frac{i\pi}{4}}}$$

   and hence

$$a_n = 2^{\frac{n}{2}}\left(\cos\frac{n\pi}{4} + 2\sin\frac{n\pi}{4}\right).$$

5. Let $a_0 = a$, $a_1 = b$, $a_2 = c$ and $a_{n+3} = da_{n+2} + ea_{n+1} + fa_n$, $n \geq 0$, where a, b, c, d, e, f are constants, then the generating function for the sequence (a_n) is

$$f(x) \equiv \frac{a + (b-da)x + (c-db-ea)x^2}{1-dx-ex^2-fx^3}.$$

Exercise 10d

1. From question 3 of exercise 10c, the sequence (n^2) satisfies the recurrence relation

$$a_{n+3} = 3a_{n+2} - 3a_{n+1} + a_n.$$

   The Fibonacci sequence satisfies $a_{n+2} = a_{n+1} + a_n$.

   The sequence (3^n) satisfies $a_{n+1} = 3a_n$.

2. We have

$$\begin{aligned} c_{n+T_c} &\equiv c_n \pmod{m} \quad \text{for all } n \geq N \\ \text{and} \quad d_{p+T_d} &\equiv d_p \pmod{m} \quad \text{for all } p \geq P. \end{aligned}$$

Hence for all $q \geq Q \geq \max(N, P)$ we have

$$\begin{aligned} c_{q+[T_c,T_d]} &\equiv c_q \pmod{m} \\ \text{and} \quad d_{q+[T_c,T_d]} &\equiv d_q \pmod{m}. \end{aligned}$$

It follows from theorem 10.3 that the period of the three sequences $(c_n + d_n)$, $(c_n - d_n)$ and $(c_n d_n)$ is a factor of $[T_c, T_d]$.

3. We have $(n+m)^3 = n^3 + 3mn^2 + 3m^2n + m^3 \equiv n^3 \pmod{m}$ and hence by theorem 10.3 the period is a factor of m. (Alternatively, we may apply the result of question 2 for the product of three identical sequences, all with $c_n = n$.) Very often the period is equal to m, but not always. For example, when $m = 9$, the period is 3.

   If T is the period, so that $(n+T)^3 \equiv n^3 \pmod{m}$ for all $n \geq N$, then $T^3 + 3nT^2 + 3n^2T \equiv 0 \pmod{m}$ and, taking n to be any large enough multiple of m, we deduce that $T^3 \equiv 0 \pmod{m}$ and hence $(a_n \pmod{m})$ is a pure periodic sequence.

4. By questions 2 and 3, a_n is periodic with period a factor of 6. Working (mod 6) we have $a_0 = 0$, $a_1 = 3$, $a_2 = 0$, $a_3 = 3$, ..., so the period is 2.

5. Working (mod 10) we have for the successive terms of the Fibonacci sequence 1, 1, 2, 3, 5, 8, 3, 1, 4, 5, 9, 4, 3, 7, 0, 7, 7, 4, 1, 5, 6, 1, 7, 8, 5, 3, 8, 1, 9, 0, 9, 9, 8, 7, 5, 2, 7, 9, 6, 5, 1, 6, 7, 3, 0, 3, 3, 6, 9, 5, 4, 9, 3, 2, 5, 7, 2, 9, 1, 0, 1, 1, ... with a period of 60 (see theorem 10.5) and terms in the sequence of the form a_{14+15k} end in a zero.

6. Working (mod 7) the successive terms of the sequence are 1, 2, 3, 4, 5, 6, 0, 1, ... The linear recurrence relation in fact defines the natural numbers and so the period is 7.

Exercise 10e

1. For $a \equiv 0, 1, 2, 3, 4, 5, 6, 7, 8, 9 \pmod{10}$ the periods (mod 10) of a_n are 1, 1, 4, 4, 2, 1, 1, 4, 4, 2 respectively.

2. Since the maximum period of $n^k \pmod{10}$ for constant k is 10, and the maximum period of $a^n \pmod{10}$ for constant a is 4 the period of n^n is $[4, 10] = 20$. The sequence is pure periodic because $20^{20} \equiv 0 \pmod{10}$.

3. Working $\pmod{11}$ successive terms of the sequence $2^n + 1$ are 2, 3, 5, 9, 6, 0, 10, 8, 4, 7, 2, 3, ... with period 10, so the values of n for which $2^n + 1$ is divisible by 11 are $n = 5 + 10k$.

4. Working $\pmod{3}$ the successive terms of the sequence a_n are $0, 1, 0, 2, 0, 1, \ldots$ with period 4 and a_{2n+1} is not divisible by 3 for any n, so is certainly not divisible by 2001. (Notice that the sequence generates every other term of the Fibonacci sequence.)

5. Suppose that (a_n) is a sequence defined by the homogeneous linear recurrence relation $a_{n+3} = k_1 a_{n+2} + k_2 a_{n+1} + k_3 a_n$, $n \geq 0$, where a_0, a_1, a_2, k_1, k_2, k_3 are integers, then $(a_n \pmod{m})$ is a pure periodic sequence $\pmod{m}$ provided $(k_3, m) = 1$. The proof mirrors that for theorem 10.5.

Project 10

1. The periods $\pmod{m}$ for $m = 2, 3, 4, 5, 6, 7, 8, 9, 10$ of the Fibonacci sequence are 3, 8, 6, 20, 24, 16, 12, 24, 60. Notice that for $n \geq 3$ the period is even, and that if m_1 and m_2 are coprime, then $T(m_1 m_2) = T(m_1)T(m_2)$. Try to prove these facts. For the next question it is useful to list the numbers comprising a period. These are:

$m = 2$: $1, 1, 0.$

$m = 3$: $1, 1, 2, 0, 2, 2, 1, 0.$

$m = 4$: $1, 1, 2, 3, 1, 0.$

$m = 5$: $1, 1, 2, 3, 0, 3, 3, 1, 4, 0, 4, 4, 3, 2, 0, 2, 2, 4, 1, 0.$

$m = 6$: $1, 1, 2, 3, 5, 2, 1, 3, 4, 1, 5, 0, 5, 5, 4, 3, 1, 4, 5, 3, 2, 5, 1, 0.$

$m = 7$: $1, 1, 2, 3, 5, 1, 6, 0, 6, 6, 5, 4, 2, 6, 1, 0.$

$m = 8$: $1, 1, 2, 3, 5, 0, 5, 5, 2, 7, 1, 0.$

$m = 9$: $1, 1, 2, 3, 5, 8, 4, 3, 7, 1, 8, 0, 8, 8, 7, 6, 4, 1, 5, 6, 2, 8, 1, 0.$

$m = 10$: 1, 1, 2, 3, 5, 8, 3, 1, 4, 5, 9, 4, 3, 7, 0, 7, 7, 4, 1, 5, 6, 1, 7, 8, 5, 3, 8, 1, 9, 0, 9, 9, 8, 7, 5, 2, 7, 9, 6, 5, 1, 6, 7, 3, 0, 3, 3, 6, 9, 5, 4, 9, 3, 2, 5, 7, 2, 9, 1, 0.

2. As you might have guessed, there is a theorem that covers this part. We have $S_0 = a_0$, $S_1 = a_0 + a_1, \ldots, S_n = a_0 + a_1 + \cdots + a_n$.

   Theorem 14.3 *Let $(a_n \pmod m)$ be a pure periodic sequence of period $T(m)$. Let $a_0 + a_1 + \cdots + a_{T(m)-1} \equiv S \pmod m$. Then $(S_n \pmod m)$ is a pure periodic sequence of period $cT(m)$, where c is the least positive constant such that $cS \equiv 0 \pmod m$.*

   In particular if $S \equiv 0 \pmod m$ the period is $T(m)$ and if $(S, m) = 1$ then the period is $mT(m)$. In general $c = \frac{m}{(S,m)}$. All the theorem is saying is that it takes c blocks of the period of (a_n) to form a block that is the period of (S_n).

   $m = 2$: $S \equiv 0 \pmod 2$, so the period is 3.
   $m = 3$: $S \equiv 0 \pmod 3$, so the period is 8.
   $m = 4$: $S \equiv 0 \pmod 4$, so the period is 6.
   $m = 5$: $S \equiv 0 \pmod 5$, so the period is 20.
   $m = 6$: $S \equiv 0 \pmod 6$, so the period is 24.
   $m = 7$: $S \equiv 0 \pmod 7$, so the period is 16.
   $m = 8$: $S \equiv 0 \pmod 8$, so the period is 12.
   $m = 9$: $S \equiv 0 \pmod 9$, so the period is 24.
   $m = 10$: $S \equiv 0 \pmod{10}$, so the period is 60.

3. The table below summarises the results of this investigation.

m	$T(m)$	$S \pmod m$	Period of $(S_n \pmod m)$
2	2	1	4
3	3	2	9
4	2	1	8
5	5	0	5
6	6	1	36
7	7	0	7
8	4	6	16
9	9	6	27
10	10	5	20

Exercise 11a

1. Since '$a679b$' is divisible by 4 the digit b is 2 or 6, and since it is divisible by 9, so is $a + b + 22$. Hence when $b = 2$, $a = 3$, and when $b = 6$, $a = 8$. There are two possible numbers, namely 36 792 and 86 796.

2. (a) The final digit of N can only be 2, and, since N is divisible by 3, the number of 2s is also divisible by 3. So the smallest value of N contains one 3 and three 2s, and is 2232.

   (b) The final three digits of M form a multiple of 8, since M is divisible by 8, and the only such possibility is 888. Since M is divisible by 9, the number of 8s is also divisible by 9. So the smallest value of M contains one 9 and nine 8s, and is 8 888 889 888.

3. The sum of the digits is a multiple of 3, so at least three of the digits are 1. The last two digits are 00 since it is a multiple of 4. Hence the smallest such number is 11 100.

4. Since the number is a multiple of 5 the final digit is 0 or 5, so, since the number is non-zero, it must consist entirely of 5s. The smallest such number which is also a multiple of 7 is 555 555.

Exercise 11b

1. There are no single-digit unfortunate numbers. For a two-digit number 'ab' we have $10a + b = 13(a + b)$, which is impossible since a, b are not both zero. For a three-digit number 'abc' we have $100a + 10b + c = 13(a + b + c)$, so $29a = b + 4c$. Hence $a = 1$ by magnitude considerations, and so $b + 4c = 29$. There are exactly three solutions, yielding the numbers 117, 156 and 195.

   For a four-digit number '$abcd$' we have $1000a + 100b + 10c + d = 13(a + b + c + d)$. But now even $a = 1$ is impossible, since the left-hand side is at least 1000 and the right-hand side at most 468. For more digits, the situation becomes more untenable. So the only unfortunate numbers are the ones already found.

2. If the number is 'ab', we need $10a + b = n(a + b)$ and $10b + a = k(a + b)$. Adding, we have $11(a + b) = (n + k)(a + b)$ and so $n + k = 11$ and $k = 11 - n$.

3. Letting the number be '*abc*', we have, after a little algebra,

$$100a + 10b + c = 22(a + b + c) \tag{14.5}$$

Hence $4b + 7c = 26a$. Hence $a \leq 3$ and also c is even. We now either look at cases, or, more neatly, subtract $a + b + c$ from both sides of equation (14.5) to obtain $3(11a + b) = 7(a + b + c)$ and so $7 \mid (11a + b)$. So if $a = 1$, it follows that $b = 3$ and $c = 2$; if $a = 2$, then $b = 6$ and $c = 4$; if $a = 3$, then $b = 9$ and $c = 6$. We therefore have three numbers 132, 264 and 396.

4. Letting m be the three-digit number formed by the first three digits, we have $1000m + m + 1 = n^2$ for some positive integer n. Hence $1001m = (n - 1)(n + 1)$. Since the prime factorisation of 1001 is $7 \times 11 \times 13$, and the factors $n - 1$, $n + 1$ have highest common factor 1 or 2, two of the primes 7, 11 and 13 divide one factor and the other prime divides the other factor. (The primes cannot all divide one of the factors because that would make $m \geq 1000$.) When all six cases are analysed, it turns out that there are three solutions for the number, namely 183 184, 328 329 and 528 529.

5. Let the two numbers be $m = a^2$ and $n = b^2$, where $32 \leq a, b \leq 99$. The difference $n - m$ is then $b^2 - a^2 = (b - a)(b + a)$ and is at least 65. It can only be one of the numbers 11, 101, 110, 1001, 1010 and 1100, and we can immediately eliminate the first as too small. Note that $b - a$ and $b + a$ have the same parity, so $n - m$ is either odd or a multiple of 4; this eliminates 110 and 1010. So now there are three cases

$$(b - a)(b + a) = 101$$
$$(b - a)(b + a) = 1001 = 7 \times 11 \times 13$$
$$(b - a)(b + a) = 1100 = 2^2 \times 5^2 \times 11$$

with the prime factorisations given.

The first case has only the one solution $(a, b) = (50, 51)$ and $(m, n) = (2\,500, 2\,601)$. In the second case there are three solutions, namely $(a, b) = (32, 45)$, $(40, 51)$ or $(68, 75)$, with $(m, n) = (1\,024, 2\,025)$, $(1\,600, 2\,601)$ or $(4\,624, 5\,625)$. The third case has only one solution in the appropriate range, namely $(a, b) = (50, 60)$ yielding $(m, n) = (2\,500, 3\,600)$. There are a total of five pairs of numbers which satisfy the condition.

Exercise 11c

1. Note first that $38^2 = 1444$. If, now, $N^2 = 1000n + 444$, then it follows that $1000 \mid (N^2 - 38^2)$ and so $2^3 \times 5^3 \mid (N-38)(N+38)$. Since these two factors have the same parity they are both divisible by 4. Also, the highest common factor of the two factors is a factor of 76, and hence coprime to 5, so we need one of the factors to have a divisor of 125. To sum up, either $N - 38$ or $N + 38$ is divisible by 500, so any number whose square ends in 444 has the form $500k \pm 38$. Finally, note that

$$\begin{aligned}(500k \pm 38)^2 &= 250\,000k^2 \pm 38\,000k + 1444 \\ &\equiv 444 \pmod{1000}\end{aligned}$$

   and so all numbers of the form $500k \pm 38$ have a square ending in 444.

   If, however, N^2 ends in 4444, it is even and equal to $4M^2$, say. Then

$$\begin{aligned}M^2 &= 2500k + 1111 \\ &\equiv 11 \pmod{100}\end{aligned}$$

   and so $M^2 \equiv 3 \pmod{4}$, which is impossible. So there are no such numbers.

2. Note that, as the fraction is proper, $0 < m < n \leq 100$. The process of decimal formation is simply a sequence of divisions, with quotient and remainder, so if the block of digits 167 appears somewhere in the expansion, there are $0 < a, b < n$ such that $1000a = 167n + b$. Since $b < n \leq 100$ this implies that $1000a < 16\,800$ and so $a \leq 16$. Working modulo 167, and noting that $167 \times 6 = 1002$ we now have $2a + b \equiv 0$. But $0 < 2a + b < 132$ and so this is impossible.

3. An immediate difficulty in tackling this problem is that subtracting anything from 10^N will involve a good deal of carrying. However, $10^N - N = (10^N - 1) - (N - 1)$, and the first term on the right-hand side is just a number consisting of N 9s, and it is easy to subtract numbers from that. Suppose now that $N - 1 = 10a + b$, so the number $10^N - N$ consists exactly of $(N-2)$ 9s, $9 - a$ and $9 - b$. Then the digit sum is exactly $9N - a - b = 89a + 8b + 9$ and this is divisible by $170 = 2 \times 5 \times 17$.

Since the digit sum is even, a is odd. Letting $a = 2c + 1$, this means that $89c + 4b + 49$ is divisible by 85. Hence $85 \mid (4c + 4b + 49)$. But $0 \le c \le 4$ and $0 \le b \le 9$ so that $4c + 4b + 49$ is between 49 and 101, so it is actually equal to 85. It follows that $c + b = 9$, so the possible values of (c, b) are $(0,9)$, $(1,8)$, $(2,7)$, $(3,6)$ and $(4,5)$. Therefore the possible values of N are 20, 39, 58, 77 and 96.

4. (a) Let $f(n) = 3n^2 + n + 1$. Working modulo 10, it is clear that $f(n) \equiv 1$, 3 or 5, and since $n > 0$ we have $f(n) > 1$. Now to obtain a digisum of 2 we need $f(n) = 10^k + 1$, or equivalently $n(3n + 1) = 10^k$. But n and $3n + 1$ are coprime, so either $n = 1$ and $3n + 1 = 10^k$, which is clearly impossible, or $n = 2^k$ and $3n + 1 = 5^k$. Hence $5^k = 3 \times 2^k + 1$. For $k = 1$ this does not work. It is now straightforward to prove by induction on k that $5^k > 3 \times 2^k + 1$ for $k \ge 2$. So there is no number with a digit sum of 2. Since $f(8) = 201$ a digisum of 3 is possible, so this is the smallest it could be.

   (b) In general digit sums of very big numbers are hard to calculate but for numbers of the form $n = 10^k - 1$ it is relatively easy. For such an n,

$$\begin{aligned} f(n) &= 3(10^k - 1)^2 + 10^k - 1 + 1 \\ &= 3 \times 10^{2k} - 5 \times 10^k + 3. \end{aligned}$$

   The resulting number will consist of a 2 followed by $(k - 1)$ 9s, then a 5, then $(k - 1)$ 0s and finally a 3. The digit sum of this is $9k + 1$, and thus any digit sum which is congruent to 1 (mod 9) can be created. In particular, if we take $k = 222$ we obtain the digit sum of 1999 which is required.

Exercise 12a

1. We use the factorisation

$$\begin{aligned} 3^{32} - 2^{32} &= \left(3^{16} + 2^{16}\right)\left(3^8 + 2^8\right)\left(3^4 + 2^4\right)\left(3^2 + 2^2\right)(3+2)(3-2) \\ &= \left(3^{16} + 2^{16}\right) \times 6817 \times 97 \times 13 \times 5 \times 1 \end{aligned}$$

so we immediately have three prime factors 5, 13 and 97, and the fourth comes from the fact that $6817 = 17 \times 401$.

2. Two primes which differ by 2 are both odd, so n is even and $n = 2m$. Then $N = n^2\left(n^2 + 16\right) = 16m^2\left(m^2 + 4\right)$ and is divisible by 16. Of the three consecutive integers $n - 1$, n, $n + 1$, one is divisible by 3. As $n - 1$ and $n + 1$ are both primes at least as big as 7 (since $n > 6$) they are not divisible by 3. Hence n is divisible by 3, so $m = 3k$ and $N = 144k^2\left(9k^2 + 4\right)$ and is divisible by 144.

   Hence it remains to prove that N is divisible by 5. One of the five consecutive integers $n - 2$, $n - 1$, n, $n + 1$, $n + 2$ is divisible by 5. Again we use the fact that $n > 6$, so $n - 1 > 5$ and so $n - 1$ and $n + 1$ are primes bigger than 5. If n is divisible by 5, we are finished, so we assume that n is either $5k - 2$ or $5k + 2$. Then $n^2 + 16 = 25k^2 \pm 20k + 20$, which is divisible by 5 and we are done.

   A counterexample to the converse result is when $n = 120$; it is obvious that N divides by 720, but neither 119 nor 121 is prime.

3. First we note that $5^{3k} - 4^{3k}$ has a factor of $5^3 - 4^3 = 61$. So the result is clearly true if $n = 3k$.

   Now neither $5^{3k+1} - 4^{3k+1} = 5\left(5^{3k} - 4^{3k}\right) + 4^{3k}$ nor $5^{3k+2} - 4^{3k+2} = 25\left(5^{3k} - 4^{3k}\right) + 9 \times 4^{3k}$ is divisible by 61, so the only cases with a factor of 61 are when $n = 3k$.

4. If $n + 2008$ is a factor of $n^2 + 2008$, it also divides

$$\left(n^2 + 2008\right) - (n + 2008) = n^2 - n,$$

   and the same is true of $n + 2009$. But $n + 2008$ and $n + 2009$ are coprime, so $(n + 2008)(n + 2009) \mid \left(n^2 - n\right)$. Hence $n^2 - n = 0$, so $n = 1$ since it is positive.

5. The required results for small values of n are:

n	$m \mid$
1	$1 - ab$
2	$1 - 2ab^2$
3	$2 - 3ab^3$

Hence $m \mid \big(2b(1-ab) - (1-2ab^2)\big)$ so $m \mid (2b-1)$.

Also $m \mid \big(3b(1-2ab^2) - 2(2-3ab^3)\big)$ so $m \mid (3b-4)$.

It follows that $m \mid \big(3(2b-1) - 2(3b-4)\big)$ and so $m \mid 5$. Hence $m = 5$ since $m > 1$. Now, since $5 \mid (2b-1)$ and $0 < b < 5$ it follows that $b = 3$. And finally, since $5 \mid (1-3a)$ and $0 < a < 5$ it follows that $a = 2$.

Thus the values of a, b and m are unique, but now we must prove that $5 \mid \big(F_n - 2n \times 3^n\big)$ for all $n \geq 1$. This is done by induction. It is true for $n = 1$ and 2, so now we assume that it is true for $n = k$ and $k+1$ and show that it is true for $n = k+2$. We have

$$F_k \equiv 2k \times 3^k \pmod 5$$

$$\text{and} \qquad F_{k+1} \equiv 2(k+1) \times 3^{k+1} \pmod 5.$$

It follows, working modulo 5, that

$$\begin{aligned} F_{k+2} &= F_k + F_{k+1} \\ &\equiv 2k \times 3^k + 2(k+1) \times 3^{k+1} \\ &\equiv 3^k(8k+6) \\ &\equiv 3^k(18k+36) \\ &\equiv 2(k+2) \times 3^{k+2} \end{aligned}$$

and the induction is complete.

Exercise 12b

1. (a) The factors of pq which are less than it are 1, p and q, so $S(pq) = 1 + p + q$. Since $p, q > 1$, and they are not both equal to 2, we have $(p-1)(q-1) > 1$ and so $pq > p + q$. Hence $pq \geq 1 + p + q$ and so pq is not abundant.

(b) Note that $S(m) > m$ since m is abundant. Suppose that the set of factors of m less than m is $\{a_1, a_2, \ldots, a_n\}$, where $a_1 = 1$. Then the factors of pm less than pm consist of the numbers in the lists $\{a_1, a_2, \ldots, a_n\}$ and $\{pa_1, pa_2, \ldots, pa_n\}$ and also m, which does not appear in either list. But the sum of these is

$$\begin{aligned} S(pm) &= (1+p)S(m) + m \\ &> (1+p)m + m \\ &= (2+p)m. \end{aligned}$$

2. Let the arithmetic progression be

$$p,\ p+d,\ p+2d,\ p+3d,\ p+4d,\ p+5d,\ p+6d.$$

Note first that p itself is prime, and that $p \geq 7$ since $p+2d$, $p+3d$ and $p+5d$ are primes.

We now concentrate on the common difference d, which is even (since otherwise $p+d$ is even), a multiple of 3 (since otherwise one of $p, p+d, p+2d$ is a multiple of 3) and a multiple of 5 (since otherwise one of $p, p+d, p+2d, p+3d, p+4d$ is a multiple of 5). Hence d is a multiple of 30. If $p = 7$, we try various values for d. When d is 30, 60 or 90, we obtain $187 = 11 \times 17$ as a member of the sequence, and this is not prime. When $d = 120$ we have the same problem with $247 = 13 \times 19$. When $d = 150$ we obtain the primes

$$7, 157, 307, 457, 607, 757, 907.$$

However, it is possible that with a larger p and smaller d we might obtain a smaller solution to the problem. The next larger value of p is 11, and now, for similar reasons to the ones above, d has a factor of 7 so is a multiple of 210. But $210 > 150$, so the largest term will be larger than 907, and larger values of p will clearly result in even larger values of this term. So the solution is 907.

(This problem was inspired by the Green-Tao theorem of 2004 that there are arbitrarily long sequences of primes in arithmetic progression.)

3. Note that x and y are both greater than N, and rearrange the given equation as

$$(x-N)(y-N) = N^2.$$

Hence both $x - N$ and $y - N$ are positive factors of N^2. The number of solutions is therefore the same as the number of positive factors of N^2. Consider the prime factorisation of $N = p_1^{\alpha_1} p_2^{\alpha_2} \cdots p_n^{\alpha_n}$, so $N^2 = p_1^{2\alpha_1} p_2^{2\alpha_2} \cdots p_n^{2\alpha_n}$. The number of factors is

$$(2\alpha_1 + 1)(2\alpha_2 + 1) \cdots (2\alpha_n + 1),$$

which has to equal $2005 = 5 \times 401$. Hence each $2a_i \equiv 0 \pmod 4$ and so all the a_i are even and N is a perfect square. (Note that we could easily list the solutions, but that is not necessary.)

4. First we use the inequalities

$$\frac{m}{n} - \frac{59}{80} < \frac{45}{61} - \frac{59}{80} \quad \text{and} \quad \frac{45}{61} - \frac{m}{n} < \frac{45}{61} - \frac{59}{80}$$

to give $80m - 59n < \frac{n}{61} \leq 2$ and $45n - 61m < \frac{n}{80} \leq 2$. Note also that $80m - 59n > 0$ and $45n - 61m > 0$.

Now, by the Euclidean algorithm, the equation $45n - 61m = 1$ has the general solution $(n, m) = (19 + 61s, 28 + 45s)$ and $45n - 61m = 2$ has solution $(n, m) = (38 + 61s, 28 + 45s)$. Similarly the two equations $80m - 59n = 1, 2$ have solutions $(n, m) = (-19 + 80t, -14 + 59t)$ and $(-38 + 80t, -28 + 59t)$. For $n < 200$ the only possible values of s and t are 1 and 2. Now a quick search reveals that the only common solution is when $s = t = 2$, which yields the fraction $\frac{104}{141}$.

Note that this could easily have been constructed from the original fractions $\frac{59}{80}$ and $\frac{45}{61}$ by adding the numerators and denominators. This process always yields a fraction in between the original two, but it does not, of course, prove uniqueness of the result.

5. The expression for n factorises as

$$m^6 - 1 = (m - 1)(m + 1)\left(m^2 - m + 1\right)\left(m^2 + m + 1\right)$$

and, for $m \geq 3$, these factors are in order of increasing magnitude. Note the following facts about these factors:

(a) $m^2 - m + 1$ and $m^2 + m + 1$ are odd and, since they differ by $2m$, coprime;

(b) $m - 1$ and $m + 1$ are either coprime or have a highest common factor of 2;

(c) $m^2 - m + 1 = (m-1)m + 1$ so $m - 1$ and $m^2 - m + 1$ are coprime;

(d) $m^2 + m + 1 = (m+1)m + 1$ so $m + 1$ and $m^2 + m + 1$ are coprime;

(e) $m^2 - m + 1 = (m+1)(m-2) + 3$ so the only possible shared prime factor of $m + 1$ and $m^2 - m + 1$ is 3. If 3 is a factor of $m + 1$, then $m \equiv 2 \pmod 3$. Now, substituting $m = 3r - 1$, we obtain $m^2 - m + 1 = 9r^2 - 9r + 3$, so the largest power of 3 which divides into $m^2 - m + 1$ is 3 itself;

(f) $m^2 + m + 1 = (m-1)(m+2) + 3$ so the only possible shared prime factor of $m - 1$ and $m^2 + m + 1$ is 3. But a similar argument shows again that the largest power of 3 which divides into $m^2 + m + 1$ is 3.

Now we consider various values of p such that $p^k \mid m^6 - 1$.

If $p > 3$, then p^k divides into exactly one of the factors, so its maximum value is $m^2 + m + 1$, but then $p^{3k} = \left(m^2 + m + 1\right)^3 < 8(m^6 - 1) = 8n$, as required. The same argument applies if 3^k divides into only one of the factors.

If $p = 3$ and there are two factors divisible by 3, then $m = 3^{k-1} \pm 1$ and we need to show that $3^{3k} < 8\left[\left(3^{k-1} \pm 1\right)^6 - 1\right]$. This is clearly true.

If $p = 2$, then p^k arises from the first two factors alone. Moreover, they do not share a factor of 4, so the largest possible value of 2^k is $2(m+1)$, and then $p^{3k} = 8(m+1)^3 < 8(m^6 - 1) = 8n$, as required.

Exercise 12c

1. The sequence of powers of 3, reduced modulo 10, is $3, 9, 7, 1, 3, \ldots$, and that of powers of 17 is $7, 9, 3, 1, 7, \ldots$. In both cases there is a cycle of length 4. The sequence for $3^n + 2 \times 17^n$ is $7, 7, 3, 3, \ldots$, but no perfect squares end in either 3 or 7.

2. If $m = n = 1$, then the expression takes the value 7. As the expression is clearly odd, we know that its smallest value is either 1, 3, 5 or 7. Since $5^n \equiv 0 \pmod 5$ and $12^m \not\equiv 0 \pmod 5$, the expression cannot be 5, and for a similar reason it cannot be 3. So we

explore the possibility that it is 1. This would mean that $5^n \equiv \pm 1 \pmod{12}$ and $12^m \equiv \pm 1 \pmod{5}$. Looking at the sequence of powers of 5, reduced modulo 12, we see that $5^n \equiv +1$ for even n, and looking at the sequence of powers of 12, reduced modulo 5, we have $12^m \equiv +1$ for $m \equiv 0 \pmod{4}$ and $12^m \equiv -1$ for $m \equiv 2 \pmod{4}$. Hence both $m = 2u$ and $n = 2v$ are even, and we have $12^{2u} - 5^{2v} = (12^u - 5^v)(12^u + 5^v) = \pm 1$. This is clearly impossible, so the smallest value of the expression is 7.

3. If $2 + 2\sqrt{1 + 12n^2}$ is an integer, then so is $2\sqrt{1 + 12n^2}$, so $\sqrt{1 + 12n^2}$ is also an integer. Hence $1 + 12n^2$ is an odd perfect square. Letting $1 + 12n^2 = (2k + 1)^2$, we obtain $3n^2 = k(k + 1)$. Since k and $k + 1$ are coprime, one is a square and one is three times a square.

   If $k = u^2$, then $k \equiv 0$ or $1 \pmod{3}$. However, $k + 1 \equiv 0 \pmod{3}$ and we have a contradiction. Hence $k + 1 = u^2$ and so the original expression is $4u^2$, a perfect square.

   This is sufficient for a proof of the problem. If, however, we wish to characterise the set of such perfect squares, we see that $k = 3v^2$ and therefore have to solve a Pell equation $u^2 - 3v^2 = 1$.

4. Let $N = 2^{a_1} + 2^{a_2} + \cdots + 2^{a_{2004}}$, where $a_1 > a_2 > \cdots > a_{2004} \geq 0$ and $a_1 = 4007$ since the binary representation has exactly 4008 digits. Since $2004 = 3 \times 2^2 \times 167$ it immediately follows that $a_{2004} \geq 2$. Considering the sequence of powers of 2, reduced modulo 3, we see that we must have an equal number of odd and even values of a_i, in order to ensure divisibility by 3.

   The divisibility by 167 is the tricky part to achieve. By Fermat's little theorem, we have $2^{166} \equiv 1 \pmod{167}$, so $M = 2^{166} - 1 = 2^{165} + 2^{164} + \cdots + 2^1 + 1$ is certainly a multiple of 167. We now construct a number beginning with 2^{4007} which is a multiple of M, namely

$$M(2^{3842} + 2^{3676} + \cdots + 2^{2016}) = 2^{4007} + 2^{4006} + \cdots + 2^{2016}.$$

   We have now achieved a binary number which divides by 2004 and with a total of 4008 digits. However, it only has 1992 1s, but this can easily be remedied by adding another number divisible by 2004 with exactly 12 1s. By experimentation, one which works is

$$2^{32} + 2^{31} + 2^{30} + 2^{27} + 2^{23} + 2^{20} + 2^{13} + 2^{10} + 2^7 + 2^6 + 2^5 + 2^4.$$

This has equal numbers of odd and even indices, and so divides by 3, and it clearly divides by 4. The residues modulo 167 have to be calculated, but this is not as difficult as it sounds, and they do add to zero.

5. Clearly all numbers in such a sequence are rational, so write $a_k = \frac{p}{q}$ with p and q coprime. Then $a_{k+1} = \frac{2p^2-q^2}{q^2}$. The highest common factor of $2p^2 - q^2$ and q^2 is either 1 or 2, so at most we will have a single cancellation when a_{k+1} is formed from a_k. If $q > 2$, then the denominator of a_{k+1}, even after such a cancellation, will be greater than that of a_k, and so the sequence of denominators will be strictly increasing, and equality is impossible. Also, if $|a_k| > 1$, then $a_{k+1} > |a_k|$ and again the sequence will be strictly increasing. So, if terms repeat, then the starting value a_0 has denominator at most 2 and lies between -1 and $+1$ inclusive. There are now five values to test:

a_0	sequence
-1	$-1, 1, 1, 1, \ldots$
$-\frac{1}{2}$	$-\frac{1}{2}, -\frac{1}{2}, -\frac{1}{2}, \ldots$
0	$0, -1, 1, 1, 1, \ldots$
$\frac{1}{2}$	$\frac{1}{2}, -\frac{1}{2}, -\frac{1}{2}, -\frac{1}{2}, \ldots$
1	$1, 1, 1, \ldots$

Exercise 13a

1. If the lengths of the two shorter sides are a and b, the condition can be expressed as
$$a^2 + b^2 = \left[\tfrac{1}{2}ab - (a+b)\right]^2,$$
which simplifies to $a = 4 + \frac{8}{b-4}$. Thus $b - 4$ is a (possibly negative) factor of 8, so that $b = 2, 3, 5, 6, 8,$ or 12. In the first two cases a is negative, so these can be discarded. There are only two solutions: a $5, 12, 13$ triangle and a $6, 8, 10$ triangle.

2. This can be rearranged to give
$$m = \frac{12n}{n-48} = 12 + \frac{576}{n-48}.$$
Thus $n - 48$ is an odd factor of 576. Since $576 = 3^2 \times 2^6$ we have $n - 48 = 1, 3$ or 9 and so $n = 49, 51, 57$. This gives the possible values of (m, n) as $(588, 49)$, $(204, 51)$ and $(76, 57)$.

3. We have $n = \frac{m(m-1)}{3m-1}$. But m and $3m - 1$ are coprime, so $3m - 1$ is a factor of $m - 1$ and $\frac{m-1}{3m-1}$ is an integer. Clearly $\frac{m-1}{3m-1} = 0$ only if $m = 1$. However, the inequality
$$-1 < \frac{m-1}{3m-1} < 1$$
has solution $m < 0$ or $m > \frac{1}{2}$. Hence we need only check $m = 0$ and 1, giving solutions $(m, n) = (0, 0)$ and $(1, 0)$.

4. Given that Paul starts with £a and Jenny starts with £b, we have
$$a + 3 = n(b-3)$$
$$b + n = 3(a-n).$$
Eliminating a gives
$$b = \frac{13n+9}{3n-1} = 4 + \frac{n+13}{3n-1}.$$
For b to be an integer we solve the inequality
$$-1 < \frac{n+13}{3n-1} < 1$$

to limit what n can be, and we find that $n < -3$ or $n > 7$. Since $n > 0$ this means we need to check values of n between 1 and 7. For 1, 2, 3 and 7 we get a and b to be positive integers.

5. Eliminating z and rearranging, we obtain $y = 12 + \frac{66}{x-12}$ thus $x - 12$ is a (not necessarily positive) factor of 66. It follows that $x = 13$, 14, 15, 18, 23, 34, 45 or 78 (note that 1 and 6 result in negative z). The full set of solutions is $(x, y, z) = (13, 78, 79)$, $(14, 45, 47)$, $(15, 34, 37)$, $(18, 23, 29)$, and the same triples with x and y interchanged.

6. Some rearrangement gives $m^2 + m + 1 = (n^2 + n + 1)^2$. But the simple size argument $m^2 < m^2 + m + 1 < (m+1)^2$ shows that $m^2 + m + 1$ cannot be a perfect square. Hence there are no solutions for positive integers n and m.

Exercise 13b

1. Substituting small values makes it clear that the sequence is simply

$$1 + 1 + \cdots + 1 + 2 + \cdots + 2 + 3 + \cdots$$

and so the exercise is simply one of counting up how many 1s, 2s, 3s, and so on there are. Note also that as another term is added, the sum increases, so there is at most one solution. Now $\lfloor \sqrt[3]{m} \rfloor = r$ only for $r^3 \le m < (r+1)^3$ and so the r can appear $(r+1)^3 - r^3$ times. Starting with $r = 1$ soon gives the solution. We need to add the 1s, 2s, 3s and 4s to get $7 + 38 + 111 + 244 = 400$. Hence $n^3 - 1 = 124$ and so $n = 5$.

2. Set $m = 6x^3$ and $n = 36y^3$ and equate coefficients of $\sqrt[3]{6}$, $\sqrt[3]{36}$ and 1. This gives $x = y = 2$ so $m = 48$ and $n = 288$ will work.

3. Substituting in small values of z we find solutions for $z = 1, 2$ or 5, but not for $z = 3$ or 4. This might suggest looking at $z = n^2 + 1$, in which case

$$\begin{aligned} z^5 + z &= (n^2+1)\left[(n^2+1)^4 + 1\right] \\ &= \left[n(n^2+1)^2 - 1\right]^2 + \left[(n^2+1)^2 + n\right]^2, \end{aligned}$$

where we have used the identity

$$\left(a^2+b^2\right)\left(c^2+d^2\right)=(ac-bd)^2+(ad+bc)^2,$$

a version of identity (5.2) on page 38.

Thus $x = n\left(n^2+1\right)^2-1$, $y = \left(n^2+1\right)^2+n$, $z = n^2+1$ exhibits an infinite set of solutions; the lack of common factors can easily be established.

Exercise 13c

1. (a) This follows in the same way as example 13.7 on page 127. The only solutions are $a = 1$ and $b = 2$, or *vice versa*.

   (b) On the supposition that there is a link between parts (a) and (b), and noticing that $35 = 27+8$ and $9 = 1+8$, it seems sensible to try to write the left-hand side as the sum of two cubes of linear expressions in x and y. Since $35x^3 = 27x^3+8x^3$ and $9y^3 = 8y^3+y^3$ it is relatively easy to show, after some experimentation, that you want $2x+y$ and $3x+2y$. Thus either $2x+y=1$ and $3x+2y=2$, or else $2x+y=2$ and $3x+2y=1$. The solutions are $(x,y)=(0,1)$ or $(3,-4)$.

2. Consider the equation modulo 4.

3. When $y = 0$, we have $2^x = (z-1)(z+1)$ and so $z-1$, $z+1$ are powers of 2 that differ by 2. Hence $z = 3$ and $x = 3$ giving $(x,y,z) = (3,0,3)$ as a solution.

   Otherwise we have $z^2-2^x \equiv 0 \pmod 3$ and since squares are either 0 or 1 $\pmod 3$ we find that $2^x \equiv 0$ or $1 \pmod 3$. The former case is impossible and so $2^x \equiv 1 \pmod 3$. Hence x is even and equal to $2a$. Thus $3^y = \left(z-2^a\right)\left(z+2^a\right)$. Both brackets must therefore be powers of 3, but their difference is a power of 2. This leads to a contradiction unless $z-2^a = 1$. Hence $3^y = z+2^a = 1+2^{a+1}$. If $a = 0$, then we have $y = 1$ and $z = 2$, giving a solution $(x,y,z) = (0,1,2)$.

   Otherwise $2^{a+1} \equiv 0 \pmod 4$ and so $3^y \equiv 1 \pmod 4$. Hence y is even, so $y = 2b$. Hence $2^{a+1} = \left(3^b-1\right)\left(3^b+1\right)$ which implies, as above, that $3^b = 3$ so $b = 1$ and $a = 2$. This gives us a solution $(x,y,z) = (4,2,5)$.

4. Treating this as a quadratic in y, we deduce that the discriminant $p^2 + 4x^2$ is a perfect square, so there is a positive integer m such that $p^2 + 4x^2 = m^2$. This, however, means that $p, 2x, m$ is a Pythagorean triple, so there are positive integers a, b, c such that $p = a(b^2 - c^2)$, $x = abc$ and $m = a(b^2 + c^2)$. Since p is an odd prime this forces $a = 1, b - c = 1$ and $p = b + c$. Thus $b = \frac{1}{2}(p+1), c = \frac{1}{2}(p-1)$ and so $x = \frac{1}{4}(p^2 - 1)$. Substituting back and using the quadratic formula we obtain $y = \frac{1}{4}(p-1)^2$.

5. Treating this as a quadratic in x, we get the discriminant $y^2(4y^2 - 3)$, which is a perfect square exactly when $4y^2 - 3 = k^2$ for some integer k. Hence $(2y - k)(2y + k) = 3$, giving $y = 1$ or -1. Thus the only solutions are $(1, -1)$ and $(-1, 1)$.

Bibliography

Books

The books [2, 5, 6] are all highly recommended by the author of this book.

[1] R. P. Burn. *A Pathway into Number Theory*. Cambridge University Press, 1996.

This is an interesting introduction to the subject, since it proceeds by forcing the reader to work through a sequence of examples.

[2] David Burton. *Elementary Number Theory*. McGraw Hill, 2010.

[3] H. Davenport. *The Higher Arithmetic: An introduction to the theory of numbers*. Cambridge University Press, 2008.

This is a famous treatment from the 1950s, now revised to take account of recent developments.

[4] G. H. Hardy and E. M. Wright. *An Introduction to the Theory of Numbers*. Oxford University Press, 2008.

This is the classic textbook on the subject, and this recent reprint, edited by R. Heath-Brown and J. H. Silverman, brings it right up to date and includes a discussion of Andrew Wiles' proof of Fermat's Last Theorem.

[5] Ivan Niven, Herbert S. Zuckerman, and Hugh L. Montgomery. *An Introduction to the Theory of Numbers*. John Wiley & Sons, 1991.

[6] Joseph H. Silverman. *A Friendly Introduction to Number Theory*. Pearson Education, 2001.

[7] Geoff Smith. *A Mathematical Olympiad Primer*. UKMT, 2008.
Although not specifically aimed at number theory, this is an excellent source of ideas for problem solving.

Websites

[8] Chris K. Caldwell. *Mersenne Primes: History, Theorems and Lists*. URL: `http://primes.utm.edu/mersenne/index.html`.

[9] Wilfrid Keller. *Prime factors* $k \cdot 2n + 1$ *of Fermat numbers* F_m *and complete factoring status*. URL: `http://www.prothsearch.net/fermat.html`.

Index